excellence in THEORY

Music Theory, Ear Training, and History Workbook

Book Three

by Ryan Nowlin and Bruce Pearson

TABLE OF CONTENTS

Kjos MULTIMEDIA LIBRARY — Ear Training Examples & Exercises

If you are using this workbook without the guidance of a teacher, or if you wish to have the Ear Training examples for your own home practice, you may download them all for free by visiting the **Kjos Multimedia Library** at www.kjos.com.

ISBN 10: 0-8497-0524-X • ISBN 13: 978-0-8497-0524-3

©2011 Kjos Music Press, Neil A. Kjos Music Company, Distributor, 4382 Jutland Drive, San Diego, California, 92117.
International copyright secured. All rights reserved. Printed in U.S.A.

Kjos Neil A. Kjos Music Company · San Diego, California

Intervals

In music, the distance between two pitches is called an **Interval**. An interval is counted from the lower note to the upper note, including both. Use the lines and spaces of the staff to identify the interval.

LESSON & ASSIGNMENT

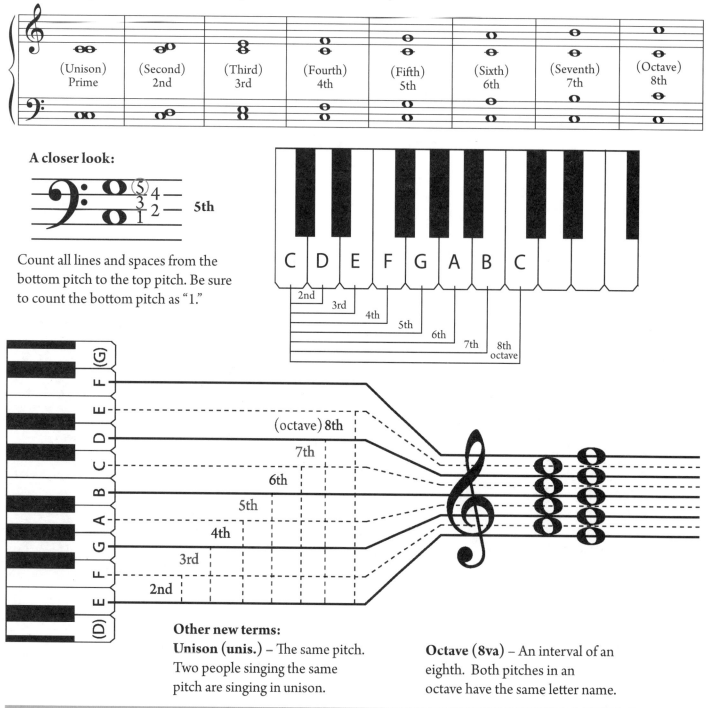

A closer look:

Count all lines and spaces from the bottom pitch to the top pitch. Be sure to count the bottom pitch as "1."

Other new terms:

Unison (unis.) – The same pitch. Two people singing the same pitch are singing in unison.

Octave (8va) – An interval of an eighth. Both pitches in an octave have the same letter name.

STUDENT ASSIGNMENT

1. Write each interval (unis., 2nd, 3rd, 4th, 5th, 6th, 7th, 8va) in the blank provided below it.

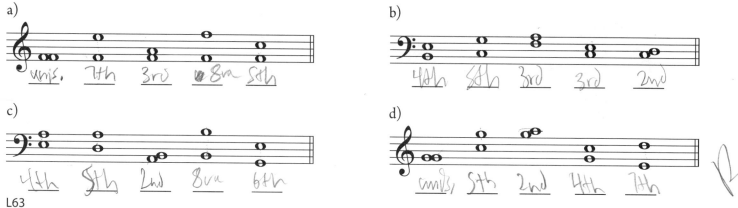

a) unis.   7th   3rd   8va   5th

b) 4th   8th   3rd   3rd   2nd

c) 4th   5th   2nd   8va   6th

d) unis.   5th   2nd   4th   7th

Harmonic & Melodic Intervals

Harmonic Intervals are created when two pitches are played/sung at the same time:

Melodic Intervals are created when two pitches are played/sung one after the other:

STUDENT ASSIGNMENT

1. Write each interval (unis., 2nd, 3rd, 4th, 5th, 6th, 7th, 8va) in the blank provided below it.

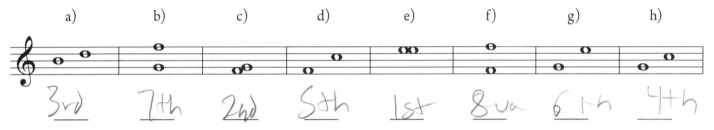

a) 3rd b) 7th c) 2nd d) 5th e) 1st f) 8va g) 6th h) 4th

2. In #1, which examples are <u>harmonic</u> intervals? Write the letters of all corresponding examples below.

b, c, e, f

3. In #1, which examples are <u>melodic</u> intervals? Write the letters of all corresponding examples below.

a, d, g, h

4. Notate the second (higher) pitch of each indicated <u>melodic</u> interval.

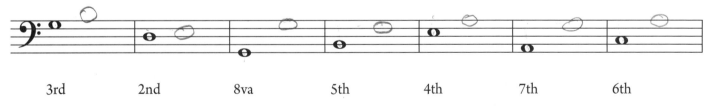

3rd   2nd   8va   5th   4th   7th   6th

5. Notate the second (higher) pitch of each indicated <u>harmonic</u> interval.

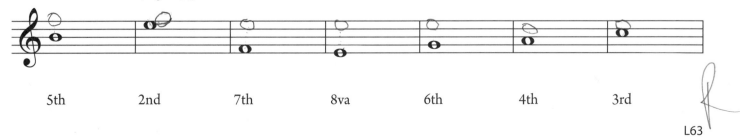

5th   2nd   7th   8va   6th   4th   3rd

Interval Identification Review

1. Identify each harmonic interval (unis., 2nd, 3rd, 4th, 5th, 6th, 7th, 8va).

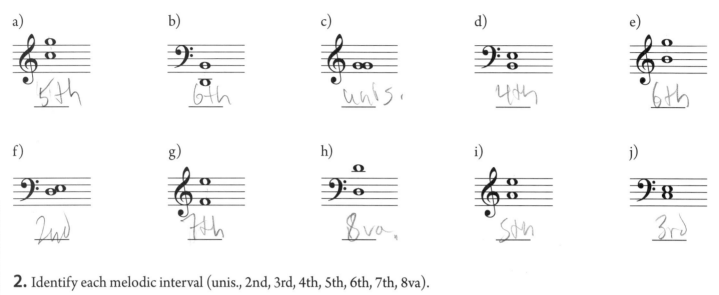

a) 5th   b) 6th   c) unis.   d) 4th   e) 6th

f) 2nd   g) 7th   h) 8va.   i) 5th   j) 3rd

2. Identify each melodic interval (unis., 2nd, 3rd, 4th, 5th, 6th, 7th, 8va).

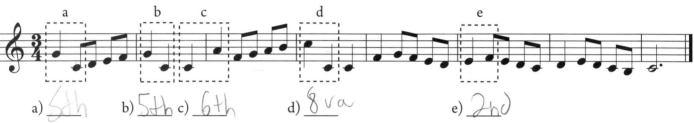

a) 5th   b) 5th   c) 6th   d) 8va   e) 2nd

3. Identify each melodic interval (unis., 2nd, 3rd, 4th, 5th, 6th, 7th, 8va).

a) 6th   b) 7th   c) unis.   d) 4th   e) 2nd

4. Given the bottom pitch of each harmonic interval, notate the <u>top</u> pitch on the appropriate line or space.

a) 3rd   b) unis.   c) 4th   d) 8va   e) 7th

5. Given the top pitch of each harmonic interval, notate the <u>bottom</u> pitch on the appropriate line or space.

a) 6th   b) 4th   c) 2nd   d) 5th   e) 8va

Perfect & Major Intervals

The interval between the first scale degree of a major scale and the unison, 4th, 5th, and octave (8va) is called a **Perfect Interval**.

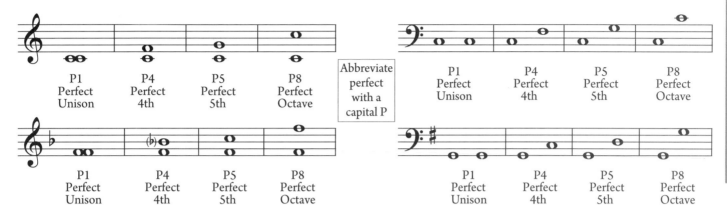

Abbreviate perfect with a capital P

The interval between the first scale degree of a major scale and the 2nd, 3rd, 6th, and 7th is called a **Major Interval**.

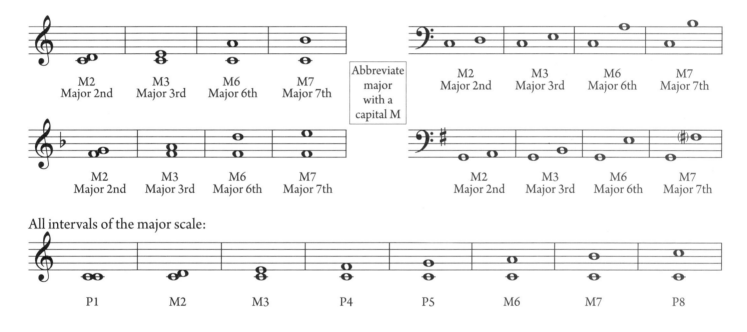

Abbreviate major with a capital M

All intervals of the major scale:

STUDENT ASSIGNMENT

1. Identify each interval (P1, M2, M3, P4, P5, M6, M7, P8, or ?). Assume the bottom note is the first scale degree of a key. If the upper note fits in that key, the interval is perfect or major. You <u>must</u> know your key signatures to get the correct answer. If the interval is neither perfect nor major, write a ? in the blank. There are only 3 ? answers below.

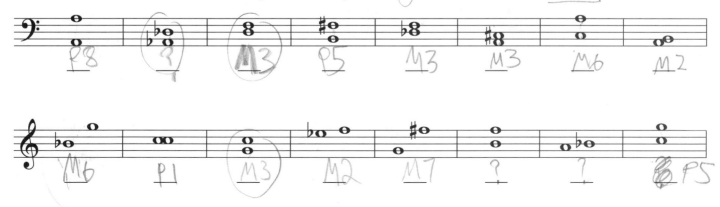

Perfect & Major Intervals Review

1. Identify each interval in the blank provided.

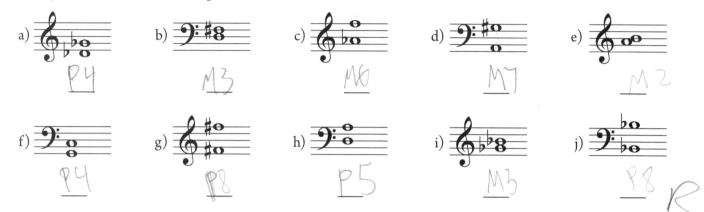

a) P4   b) M3   c) M6   d) M7   e) M2

f) P4   g) P8   h) P5   i) M3   j) P8

2. Given the bottom note, draw the <u>top</u> note of the harmonic interval in each exercise.

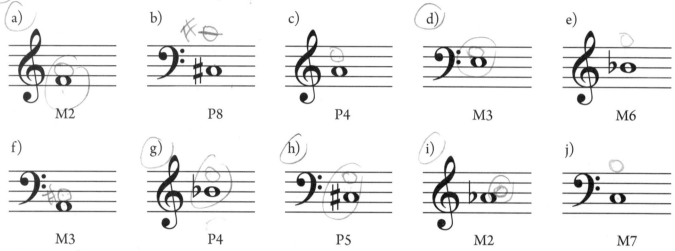

a) M2   b) P8   c) P4   d) M3   e) M6

f) M3   g) P4   h) P5   i) M2   j) M7

3. Identify the major key signature, then the intervals in each exercise.

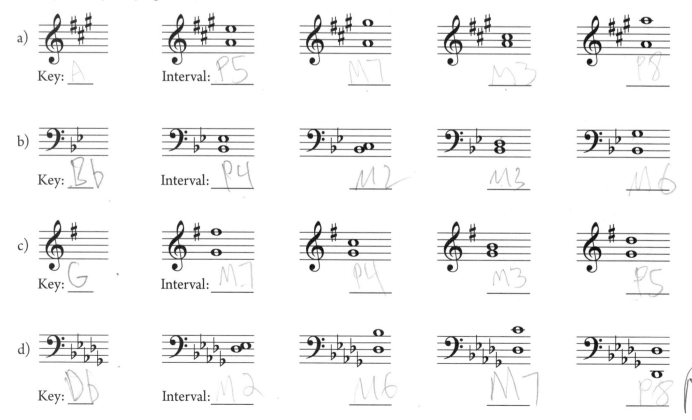

a) Key: A   Interval: P5   M7   M3   P8

b) Key: Bb   Interval: P4   M2   M3   M6

c) Key: G   Interval: M7   P4   M3   P5

d) Key: Db   Interval: M2   M6   M7   P8

Ear Training Part 9

Audio files can be found in the **Kjos Multimedia Library** at www.kjos.com.

Listen to the following examples of melodic and harmonic intervals.

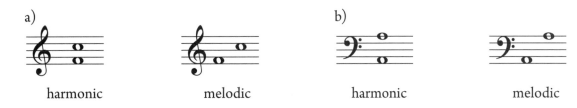

a)		b)	
harmonic	melodic	harmonic	melodic

Listen to the following perfect intervals. They will be demonstrated melodically, harmonically, and again melodically.

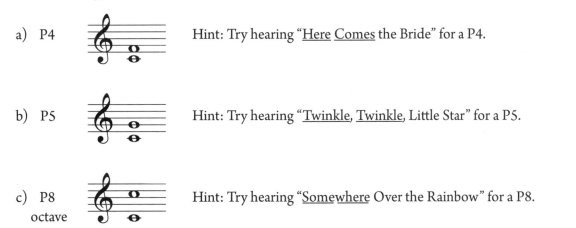

a) P4   Hint: Try hearing "<u>Here Comes</u> the Bride" for a P4.

b) P5   Hint: Try hearing "<u>Twinkle, Twinkle</u>, Little Star" for a P5.

c) P8
octave   Hint: Try hearing "<u>Somewhere</u> Over the Rainbow" for a P8.

1. Listen to each interval. Write the interval (P4, P5, P8) in the space provided. Each interval will be demonstrated melodically, harmonically, and again melodically.

a) P8   b) P4   c) P5   d) P4

e) P5   f) P4   g) P4   h) P8

Listen to the following major intervals. They will be demonstrated melodically, harmonically, and again melodically.

a) M2   Hint: Try hearing the first two notes of a major scale.

b) M3   Hint: Try hearing "<u>Oh, When</u> the Saints Go Marching In."

c) M6   Hint: Try hearing the <u>NBC</u> theme.

d) M7   Hint: Try hearing a half step down from an octave.

2. Listen to each interval. Write the interval (M2, M3, M6, M7) in the space provided. Each interval will be demonstrated melodically, harmonically, and again melodically.

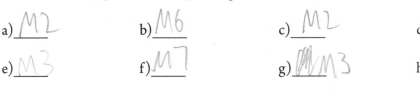

a) M2   b) M6   c) M2   d) M7

e) M3   f) M7   g) M3   h) M6

Minor Intervals

A major interval becomes a **Minor Interval** by lowering the top note by a half step.

Abbreviate minor with a lower case m

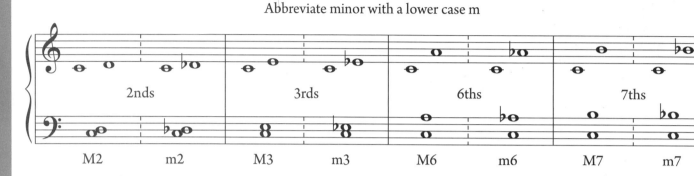

2nds   3rds   6ths   7ths

M2   m2   M3   m3   M6   m6   M7   m7

Steps to identifying an interval:

1. What is the name of the "generic" interval? (6)
2. What is the name of the bottom note? (A)
3. What is the 6th scale degree in A Major? (F♯)
4. What is the name of the top note? (F)

Since the top note is a half step lower than the 6th scale degree, the interval is m6.

Steps to writing an interval:

Step 1   Step 4

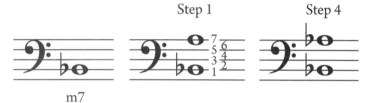

m7

1. Count from the written note and write the seventh.
2. What is the name of the bottom note? (B♭)
3. What is the 7th scale degree in B♭ Major? (A)
4. Because you are building a minor interval, lower it a half step. (A♭)

Write an A♭ above the written B♭.

STUDENT ASSIGNMENT

1. Identify each interval (P1, m2, M2, m3, M3, P4, P5, m6, M6, m7, M7, P8).

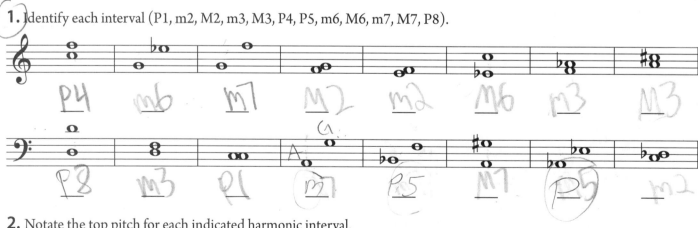

P4   m6   M7   M2   m2   M6   m3   M3

P8   m3   P1   m7   P5   M7   P5   m2

2. Notate the top pitch for each indicated harmonic interval.

m7   M6   m3   m6   M7   m2

Minor, Major, & Perfect Intervals Review

1. Identify each perfect or minor interval (P1, m2, m3, P4, P5, m6, m7, P8).

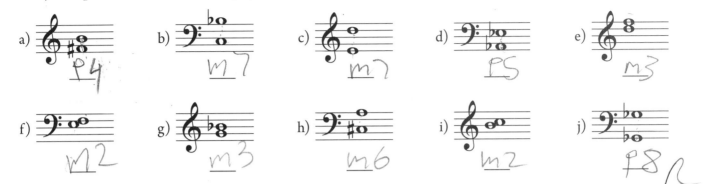

a) P4   b) m7   c) m7   d) P5   e) m3

f) M2   g) m3   h) m6   i) m2   j) P8

2. Given the bottom note, draw the top note of each harmonic interval.

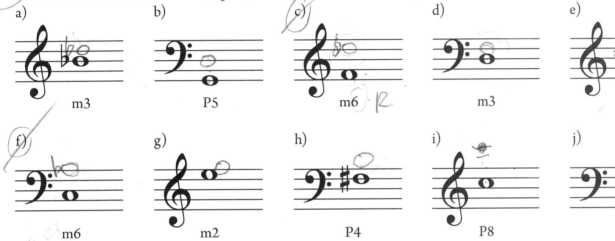

a) m3   b) P5   c) m6   d) m3   e) P5

f) m6   g) m2   h) P4   i) P8   j) m3

3. Identify each major or minor interval (M2, m2, M3, m3, M6, m6, M7, m7).

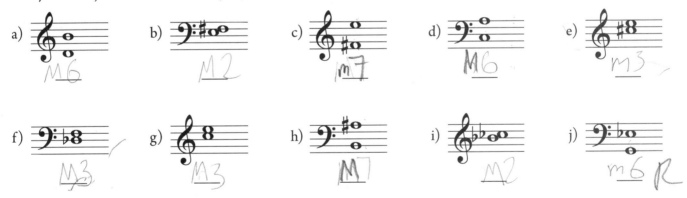

a) M6   b) M2   c) m7   d) M6   e) m3

f) M3   g) M3   h) M7   i) M2   j) m6

4. Given the bottom note, draw the top note of each harmonic interval.

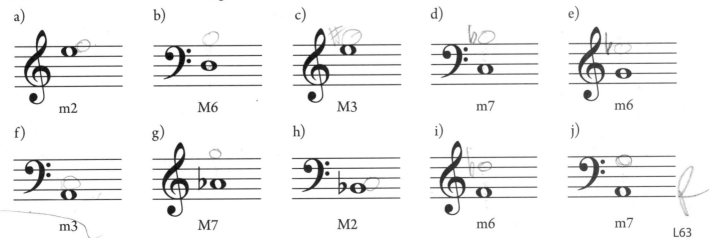

a) m2   b) M6   c) M3   d) m7   e) m6

f) m3   g) M7   h) M2   i) m6   j) m7

L63

Ear Training Part 10(a)

Audio files can be found in the **Kjos Multimedia Library** at www.kjos.com.

Listen to the following <u>minor</u> intervals. They will be demonstrated melodically, harmonically, and again melodically.

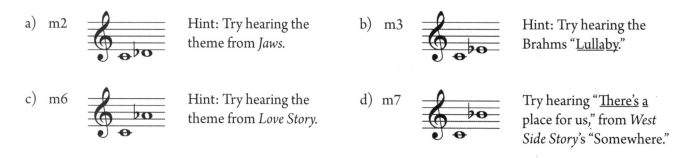

a) m2 — Hint: Try hearing the theme from *Jaws.*

b) m3 — Hint: Try hearing the Brahms "Lullaby."

c) m6 — Hint: Try hearing the theme from *Love Story.*

d) m7 — Try hearing "There's a place for us," from *West Side Story's* "Somewhere."

1. Listen to each interval performed. Write the <u>minor</u> interval (m2, m3, m6, m7) in the space provided. Each interval will be played melodically, harmonically, and again melodically.

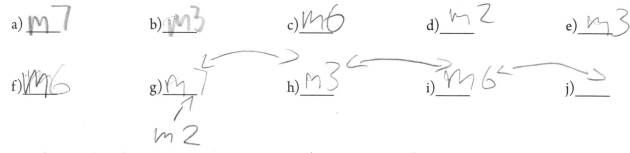

a) m7   b) m3   c) m6   d) m2   e) m3

f) m6   g) m7   h) m3   i) m6   j) _____

m2

2. Listen to each interval performed. Write the <u>major</u> interval (M2, M3, M6, M7) in the space provided.

a) M2   b) M7   c) M3   d) M6   e) M6

f) M3   g) M7   h) M2   i) M3   j) M6

3. Listen to each interval performed. Write the <u>minor</u> or <u>major</u> interval (m2, M2, m3, M3, m6, M6, m7, M7) in the space provided.

a)_____   b)_____   c)_____   d)_____

e)_____   f)_____   g)_____   h)_____

i)_____   j)_____   k)_____   l)_____

4. Listen to each interval performed. Write the <u>perfect</u> or <u>minor</u> interval (m2, m3, P4, P5, m6, m7, P8) in the space provided.

a)_____   b)_____   c)_____   d)_____   e)_____

f)_____   g)_____   h)_____   i)_____   j)_____

Augmented & Diminished Intervals

When the top note of a <u>major</u> or <u>perfect</u> interval is <u>raised</u> a half step, the result is an **Augmented Interval**.

When raising a ♯ an additional half step, a **Double Sharp** (✕) is created.

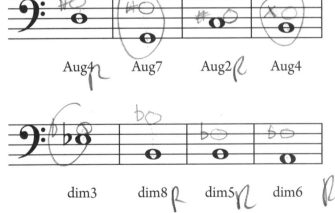

When the top note of a <u>minor</u> or <u>perfect</u> interval is <u>lowered</u> a half step, the result is a **Diminished Interval**.

When lowering a ♭ an additional half step, a **Double Flat** (♭♭) is created.

LESSON & ASSIGNMENT

STUDENT ASSIGNMENT

1. Notate the top pitch of each indicated harmonic interval.

Aug5   Aug6   Aug8   Aug3

Aug4   Aug7   Aug2   Aug4

dim4   dim5   dim2   dim7

dim3   dim8   dim5   dim6

2. Identify each augmented or diminished interval in the blank provided below it.

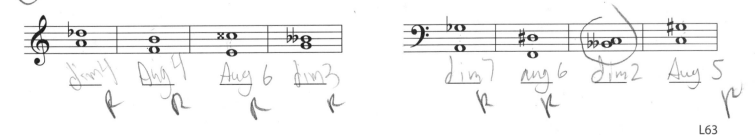

Augmented, Diminished, Minor, Major & Perfect Review

1. Given the bottom pitch of the indicated interval, notate the top pitch.

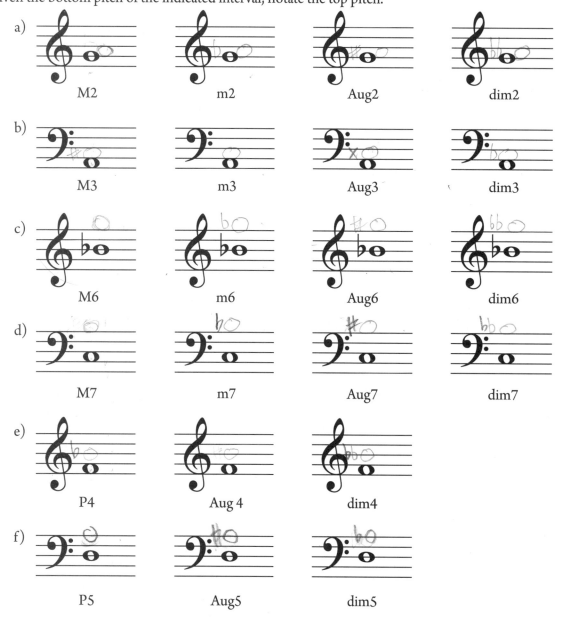

a) M2   m2   Aug2   dim2

b) M3   m3   Aug3   dim3

c) M6   m6   Aug6   dim6

d) M7   m7   Aug7   dim7

e) P4   Aug 4   dim4

f) P5   Aug5   dim5

2. Identify each interval (M, m, P, Aug, or dim) in the blank provided below it.

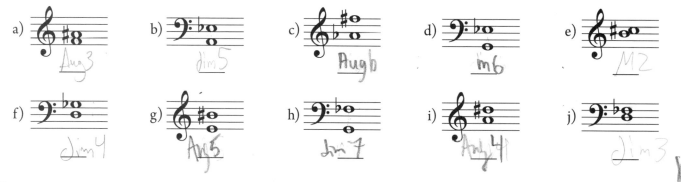

a) Aug3   b) dim5   c) Aug6   d) m6   e) M2

f) dim4   g) Aug5   h) dim7   i) Aug4   j) dim3

3. Given the bottom pitch of the indicated interval, notate the top pitch.

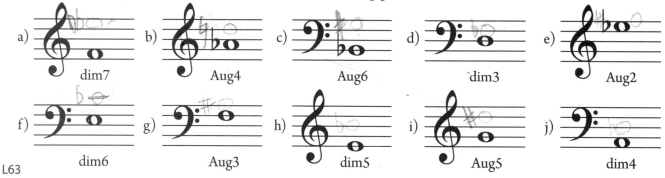

a) dim7   b) Aug4   c) Aug6   d) dim3   e) Aug2

f) dim6   g) Aug3   h) dim5   i) Aug5   j) dim4

Ear Training Part 11(a)

Audio files can be found in the **Kjos Multimedia Library** at www.kjos.com.

Listen to the following example of a **Tritone** (TT). A tritone is another name for a diminished 5th or augmented 4th. It will be played melodically, harmonically, and again melodically.

TT 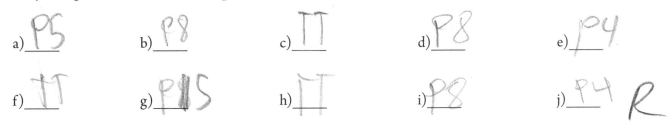 Hint: Try hearing "Maria" from *West Side Story*.

1. Identify each perfect or tritone interval performed (P4, P5, P8, TT).

a) PS   b) P8   c) TT   d) P8   e) P4

f) TT   g) P5   h) TT   i) P8   j) P4 R

2. Identify each interval performed. All intervals learned will be used (m2, M2, m3, M3, P4, TT, P5, m6, M6, m7, M7, P8).

a) PS   b) m2   c) M6   d) TT   e) M7

f) M3   g) P8   h) M7   i) P4   j) m3

k) M6   l) TT   m) M2   n) M6   o) PS

3. Identify each interval performed. All intervals learned will be used (m2, M2, m3, M3, P4, TT, P5, m6, M6, m7, M7, P8).

a) P8   b) m3   c) PS   d) TT   e) P4

f) M7   g) M6   h) m2   i) M7   j) m6

k) M2   l) M3   m) P8   n) m3   o) PS

p) M7   q) M3   r) TT   s) M2   t) m7

EAR TRAINING

3/8, 6/8, 9/8, 12/8 Time Signatures: Changing the Bottom Number

3 — 3 beats in a measure
8 — eighth note ($\frac{1}{8}$) gets the beat

Therefore: ♪ = 1 beat   ♩ = 2 beats

♪ = $\frac{1}{2}$ beat   ♩. = 3 beats

6 — 6 beats in a measure
8 — eighth note ($\frac{1}{8}$) gets the beat

9 — 9 beats in a measure
8 — eighth note ($\frac{1}{8}$) gets the beat

12 — 12 beats in a measure
8 — eighth note ($\frac{1}{8}$) gets the beat

STUDENT ASSIGNMENT

1. Draw in the missing bar lines in each exercise. Write in the counting. Clap. Place beats on rests in parentheses. For notes longer than an eighth note, place brackets around first and last beats of that note.

a)

b)

c)

d)

$\frac{3}{8}$, $\frac{6}{8}$, $\frac{9}{8}$, $\frac{12}{8}$ Time Signatures—Part 2

As the music written in these time signatures increases in tempo, the beats in each measure get grouped in threes: one strong beat followed by two weak beats. These groupings each receive one pulse resulting in a different "feel."

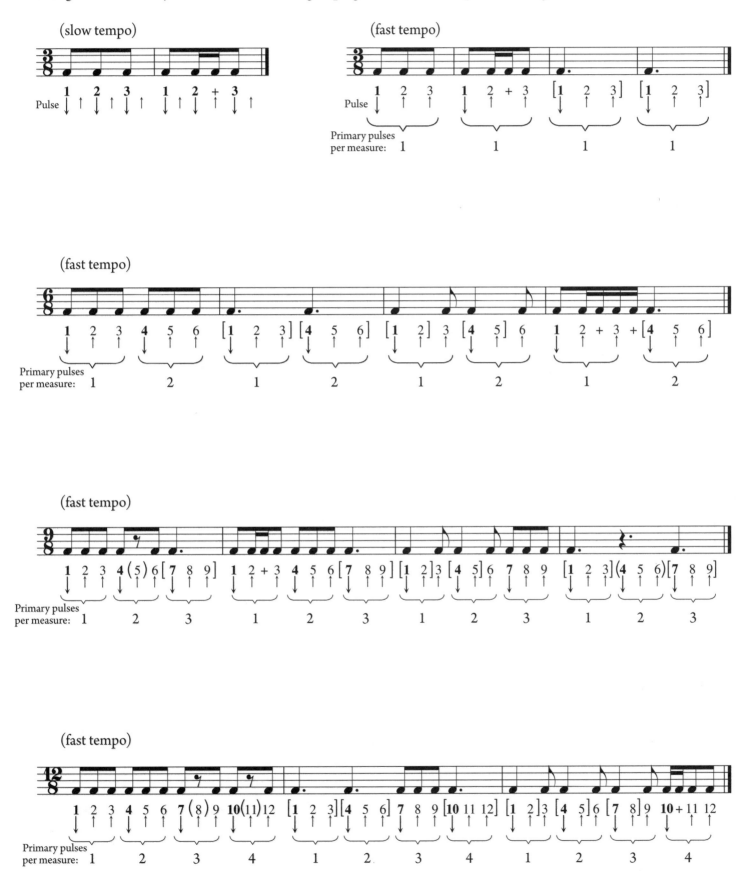

$\frac{2}{2}$ or ¢ Time Signature:
Changing the Bottom Number

$\frac{4}{4}$ is also called **Common Time** and can be written as: **C**

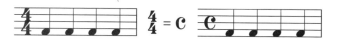

$\frac{2}{2}$ is also called **Cut Time** and can be written as: ¢

2 — 2 beats in a measure
2 — half note ($\frac{1}{2}$) gets the beat

Also known as: $\frac{2}{2}$ = ¢ = Cut Time = *Alla Breve*

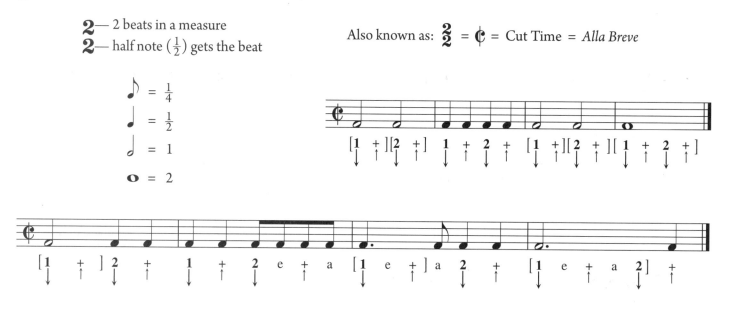

♪ = $\frac{1}{4}$

♩ = $\frac{1}{2}$

𝅗𝅥 = 1

𝅝 = 2

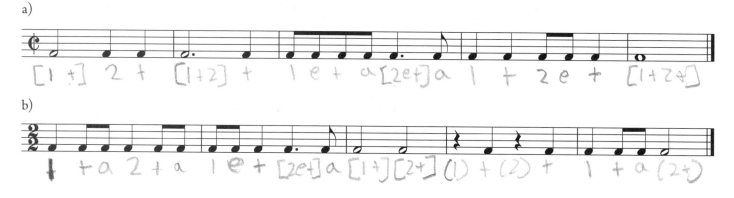

STUDENT ASSIGNMENT

1. Write in the counting and clap. Place beats on rests in parentheses. Place the counting of notes longer than a quarter note in brackets.

a)

b)

2. Draw in the missing bar lines, write in the counting, and clap. Place beats on rests in parentheses. Place the counting of notes longer than a quarter note in brackets.

a)

b)

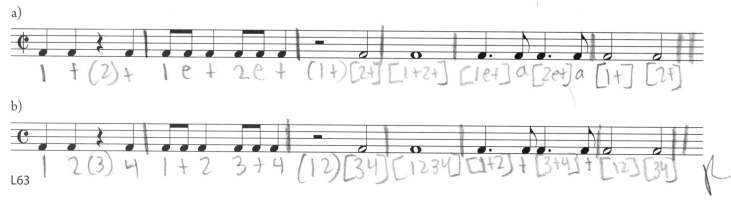

$\mathbf{C}$, $\frac{3}{8}$, $\frac{6}{8}$, $\frac{9}{8}$, $\frac{12}{8}$ Review

1. Draw in the missing bar lines, write in the counting, and clap. Place beats on rests in parentheses. Place the counting of notes longer than an eighth note in brackets.

a) Largo

b) Adagio

c) Largo

d) Adagio

2. Draw in the missing bar lines, write in the counting, group the primary pulses, and tap the rhythm on your desk. The first measure of the first exercise has been done for you.

a) Moderato

b) Allegro

c) Allegro

d) Moderato

e) Allegro

REVIEW

Ear Training Part 12

Audio files can be found in the **Kjos Multimedia Library** at www.kjos.com.

1. Listen to each rhythmic idea. For the slow versions, write in the counting. For the fast versions, write in the counting and group the primary pulses.

2. Listen to each rhythmic idea. Circle the rhythm performed.

Listen to the following examples. Both are performed at the same tempo, but each has a different time signature.

3. Listen to each rhythmic idea. Circle the rhythm performed.

Triads—Major & Minor

A **Triad** is three pitches sounding simultaneously. Each pitch of a triad is a 3rd apart. The top and bottom pitches are a 5th apart.

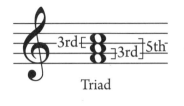

Triad

A **Major Triad** is composed of a major 3rd on the bottom and a minor 3rd on top.

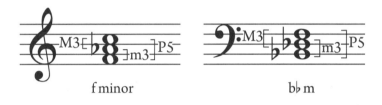

F Major   B♭ M

A triad is named after its **Root**, or bottom pitch.

A **Minor Triad** is composed of a minor 3rd on the bottom and a major 3rd on top.

f minor   b♭ m

STUDENT ASSIGNMENT

1. Name each triad. Be sure to indicate major or minor (M or m).

a) EM   b) A♭M   c) gm   d) dm   e) CM

2. Construct each <u>minor</u> triad. The first pitch is provided for each.

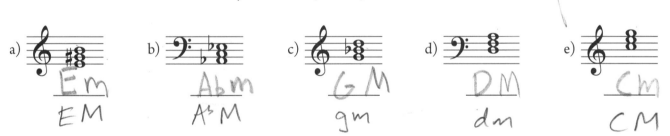

a) d minor   b) em   c) f minor   d) cm   e) a minor

3. Construct each <u>major</u> triad. The first pitch is provided for each.

a) C Major   b) FM   c) G Major   d) DM   e) E♭ Major

Major & Minor Triads Review

1. Construct each <u>major</u> triad. The first pitch is provided for each.

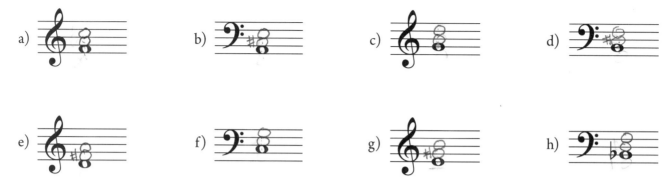

a)   b)   c)   d)

e)   f)   g)   h)

2. Construct each <u>minor</u> triad. The first pitch is provided for each.

a)   b)   c)   d)

e)   f)   g)   h)

3. Construct each <u>major</u> triad. The first pitch is provided for each.

a)   b)   c)   d)

4. Construct each <u>minor</u> triad. The first pitch is provided for each.

a)   b)   c)   d)

5. Identify each major or minor triad. Be sure to indicate M or m.

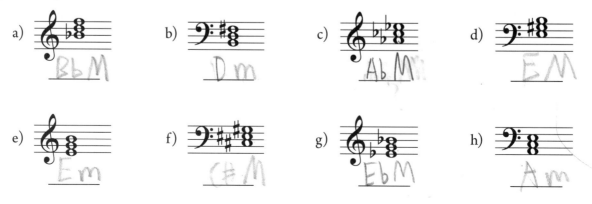

a) BbM   b) Dm   c) AbM   d) EM

e) Em   f) C#M   g) EbM   h) Am

Triads—Augmented & Diminished

An **Augmented Triad** is a major triad with a raised 5th. This results in both the bottom and top intervals being a M3. The 5th then becomes an augmented 5th. An augmented triad can be abbreviated with Aug or +.

An **Diminished Triad** is a minor triad with a lowered 5th. This results in both the bottom and top intervals being a m3. The 5th then becomes a diminished 5th. A diminished triad can be abbreviated with dim or °.

STUDENT ASSIGNMENT

1. Name each triad. Be sure to indicate Aug (+) or dim (°).

a) E° b) A+ c) G° d) C+ e) Eb+

2. Construct each <u>augmented</u> triad.

a) C Aug b) G+ c) D Aug d) Eb+ e) Ab Aug

3. Construct each <u>diminished</u> triad.

a) b dim b) c# ° c) e dim d) a° e) f# dim

Augmented & Diminished, Major & Minor Triads Review

1. Construct each <u>major</u> or <u>augmented</u> triad.

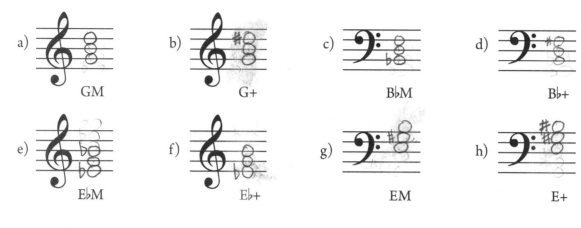

2. Construct each <u>minor</u> or <u>diminished</u> triad.

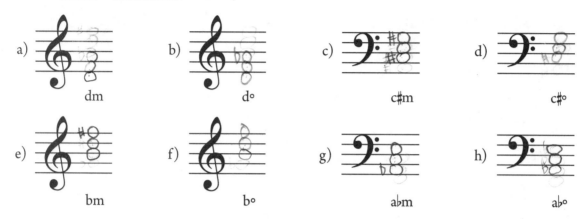

3. Fill in the missing pitch of the triad in each exercise.

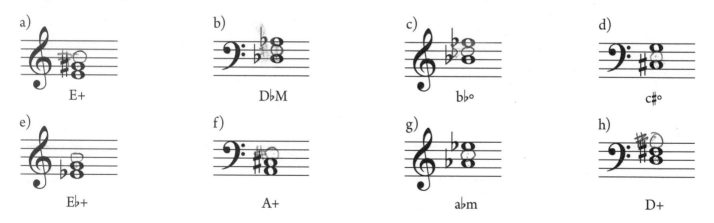

4. Identify the triad in each exercise. Be sure to indicate M, m, +, or °.

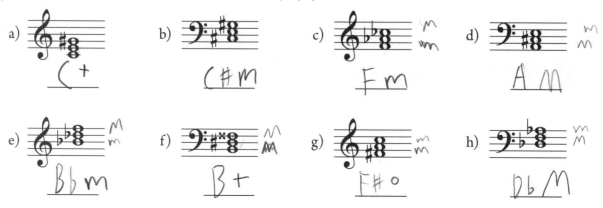

Triads in Major Scales

Triads can be built on every scale degree of a major scale. These triads (or **Chords**) use pitches from the key signature of the scale. Roman numerals are often used to identify the chords in a given key. The roman numerals refer to the scale degree of the root of each chord. <u>Major</u> chords are identified by uppercase numerals (e.g., I, IV, V). <u>Minor</u> chords are identified by lowercase numerals (e.g., ii, iii, vi). An <u>augmented</u> chord is identified by upper case numerals and a plus sign (e.g., VII+). A <u>diminished</u> chord is identified by lower case numerals and a degree sign (e.g., vii°).

The chords built on each scale degree are of the same quality (major, minor, or diminished) in <u>every major key</u>.

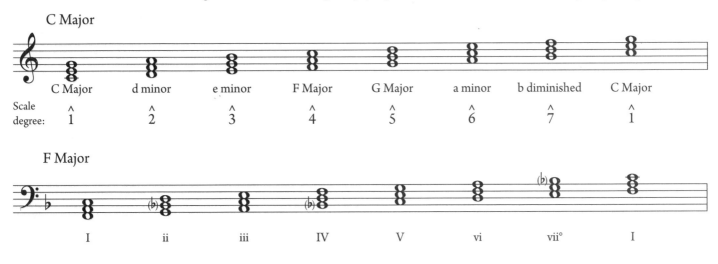

STUDENT ASSIGNMENT

1. Build triads on each scale degree of the major scales indicated. Label each chord with a roman numeral and its name.

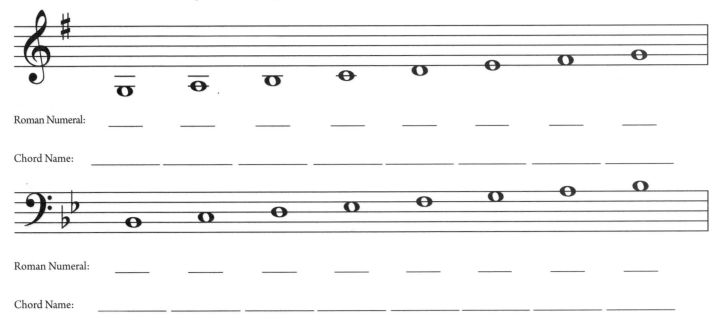

Roman Numeral: _____ _____ _____ _____ _____ _____ _____ _____

Chord Name: _____ _____ _____ _____ _____ _____ _____ _____

Roman Numeral: _____ _____ _____ _____ _____ _____ _____ _____

Chord Name: _____ _____ _____ _____ _____ _____ _____ _____

2. Using the information provided, notate the triad in each major key indicated.

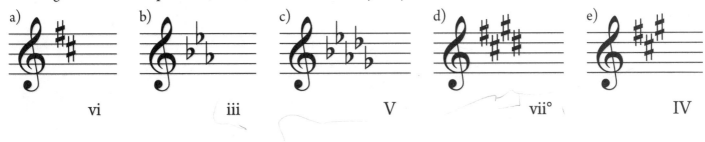

Ear Training Part 13

Audio files can be found in the **Kjos Multimedia Library** at www.kjos.com.

Listen to the following major and minor triads. Each one will be performed as a triad, a broken triad, and a triad again.

a) C Major b) c minor c) D Major d) d minor

1. Listen to each triad performed. If you hear a major triad, circle "M." If you hear a minor triad, circle "m."

a) M m   b) M m   c) M m   d) M m

e) M m   f) M m   g) M m   h) M m

Listen to each triad performed. Each one will be performed as a triad, a broken triad, and a triad again.

a) C Major b) C Aug c) c minor d) c dim

2. Listen to each triad performed. If you hear a major triad, circle "M." If you hear a minor triad, circle "m." If you hear an augmented or diminished triad, circle "+/°."

a) M m +/°   b) M m +/°   c) M m +/°

d) M m +/°   e) M m +/°   f) M m +/°

g) M m +/°   h) M m +/°   i) M m +/°

Listen to the triads in a major scale.

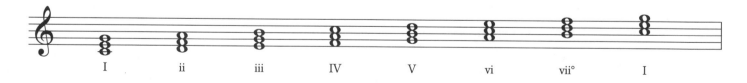

I   ii   iii   IV   V   vi   vii°   I

EAR TRAINING

Minor Scales—Relative Keys

A scale built off the sixth scale degree of a major scale is a **Minor Scale**. These scales share the same key signature.

Every major scale shares its key signature with a minor scale. These keys are called "relative."

The <u>C Major</u> scale's Relative Minor is the <u>a minor</u> scale.
The <u>a minor</u> scale's Relative Major is the <u>C Major</u> scale.

Finding a relative key signature starting from Major:

A M6 above the root of a major key indicates
the root of its relative minor. ↑M6

Example:
D Major's relative minor is b minor

Finding a relative key signature starting from minor:

A m3 above the root of a minor key indicates
the root of its relative major. ↑m3

Example:
g minor's relative major is B♭ Major

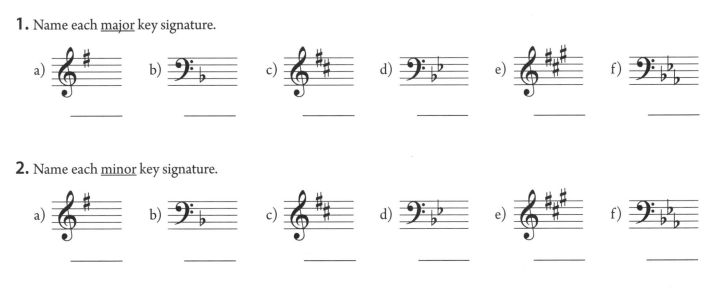

STUDENT ASSIGNMENT

1. Name each <u>major</u> key signature.

a) _____ b) _____ c) _____ d) _____ e) _____ f) _____

2. Name each <u>minor</u> key signature.

a) _____ b) _____ c) _____ d) _____ e) _____ f) _____

3. Complete the following statements.

a) A Major's relative minor is ____ minor.

b) A♭ Major's relative minor is ____ minor.

c) E♭ Major's relative minor is ____ minor.

d) b minor's relative major is ____ Major.

e) b♭ minor's relative major is ____ Major.

f) d minor's relative major is ____ Major.

Forms of Minor Scales

Natural Minor – A scale using the same notes of a major scale, but using the sixth scale degree of the major scale as its root.

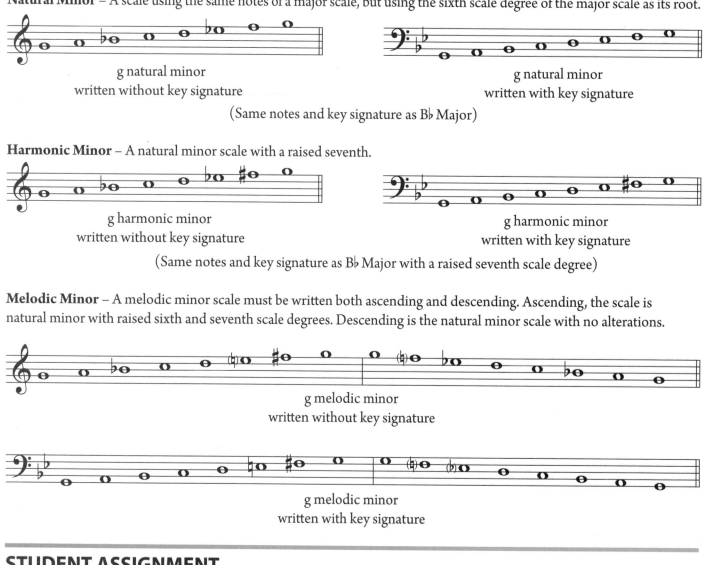

g natural minor
written without key signature

g natural minor
written with key signature

(Same notes and key signature as B♭ Major)

Harmonic Minor – A natural minor scale with a raised seventh.

g harmonic minor
written without key signature

g harmonic minor
written with key signature

(Same notes and key signature as B♭ Major with a raised seventh scale degree)

Melodic Minor – A melodic minor scale must be written both ascending and descending. Ascending, the scale is natural minor with raised sixth and seventh scale degrees. Descending is the natural minor scale with no alterations.

g melodic minor
written without key signature

g melodic minor
written with key signature

STUDENT ASSIGNMENT

1. Write the following natural minor scales. <u>Be sure to include a key signature</u>.

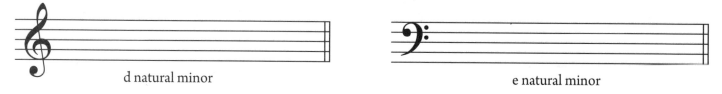

d natural minor

e natural minor

2. Write the following harmonic minor scales. <u>Be sure to include a key signature</u>.

c harmonic minor

b harmonic minor

3. Write an a melodic minor scale.

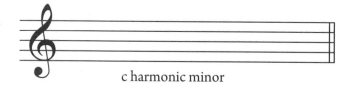

ascending

decending

Minor Keys & Scales Review

1. Identify the relative major and minor keys for each key signature indicated.

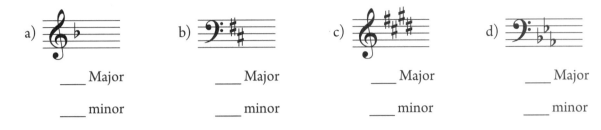

a) ___ Major   b) ___ Major   c) ___ Major   d) ___ Major

   ___ minor   ___ minor   ___ minor   ___ minor

2. Name the relative minors for each major key indicated. Draw the key signature.

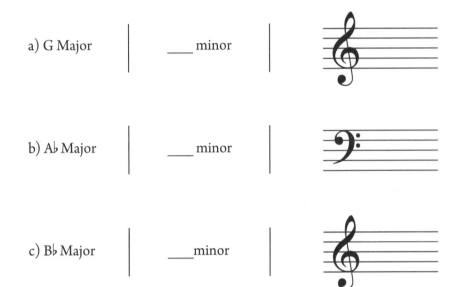

a) G Major | ___ minor |

b) A♭ Major | ___ minor |

c) B♭ Major | ___ minor |

3. <u>Without</u> using key signatures, write each scale indicated (ascending only for a–d).

a) f natural minor

b) d harmonic minor

c) c harmonic minor

d) f♯ natural minor

e) g melodic minor

    ascending   descending

f) e melodic minor

    ascending   descending

Triads in Minor Scales

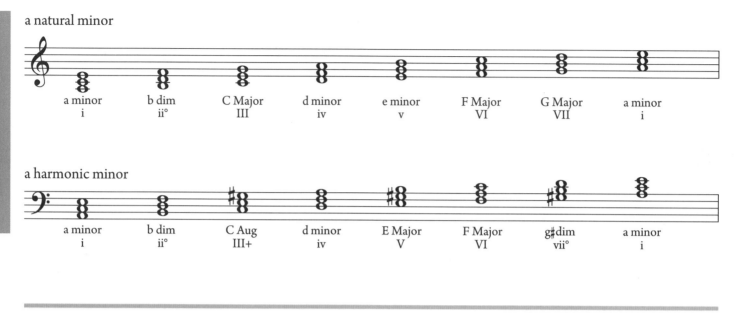

a natural minor

| a minor | b dim | C Major | d minor | e minor | F Major | G Major | a minor |
| i | ii° | III | iv | v | VI | VII | i |

a harmonic minor

| a minor | b dim | C Aug | d minor | E Major | F Major | g♯ dim | a minor |
| i | ii° | III+ | iv | V | VI | vii° | i |

STUDENT ASSIGNMENT

1. Write the chords in the following minor keys.

a) Key: _____ minor

i   iv   V   ii°

b) Key: _____ minor

i   iv   V   VI

2. Identify the chords using roman numerals. Label the key.

a) Key: _____ minor

___   ___   ___   ___

b) Key: _____ minor

___   ___   ___   ___

3. Write the following scales. Be sure to include key signatures.

a)

c natural minor (ascending only)

b)

e harmonic minor (ascending only)

c)   ascending   descending

d melodic minor

Ear Training Part 14

Audio files can be found in the **Kjos Multimedia Library** at www.kjos.com.

Listen to the following forms of the a minor scale.

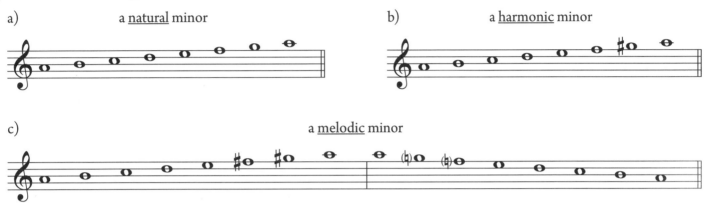

a) a <u>natural</u> minor

b) a <u>harmonic</u> minor

c) a <u>melodic</u> minor

1. Listen to each minor scale performed. Circle the form you hear.

a)	Natural	Harmonic	Melodic	b)	Natural	Harmonic	Melodic
c)	Natural	Harmonic	Melodic	d)	Natural	Harmonic	Melodic
e)	Natural	Harmonic	Melodic	f)	Natural	Harmonic	Melodic
g)	Natural	Harmonic	Melodic	h)	Natural	Harmonic	Melodic

2. Listen to each triad performed. Circle what you hear: "M" for major, "m" for minor, and "+/°" for augmented or diminished.

a) M   m   +/°   b) M   m   +/°   c) M   m   +/°

d) M   m   +/°   e) M   m   +/°   f) M   m   +/°

Listen to the triads in the c <u>natural</u> minor scale.

Listen to the triads in the c <u>harmonic</u> minor scale.

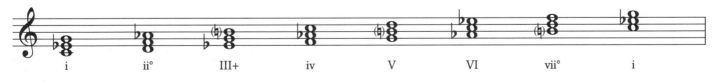

EAR TRAINING

Common Chord Progressions—Working in Major

A **Chord Progression** is a series of two or more chords played in succession. Chord progressions are like musical DNA. They are a foundation of a musical idea.

When you listen to your favorite music, be it on the radio or in a concert hall, you will most likely hear a series of chords moving in a pattern creating the basis for a melody. You can find commonalities in these chord progressions regardless of style and genre.

It is important to think of a chord progression as a journey. The destination of this journey is the **I** chord. The strongest way to approach the **I** chord is from the **V** chord. Therefore, it can be said that the most basic chord progression is **I–V–I**. With the knowledge of this musical "DNA," you will be able to use this common progression in any key.

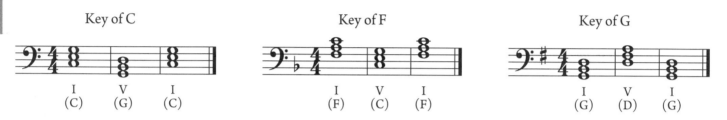

Moving from **V** to **I** offers the listener a sense of conclusion, finality, and resolution—much like a period at the end of a sentence. This type of progression that marks the end of a phrase of music is called a **Cadence**.

There are many routes to take on the journey, or progression, to the cadence. A common way to approach the **V** chord is through the **IV** chord. Therefore, a very common chord progression is **I–IV–V–I**. With the knowledge of this musical DNA, you will be able to use this common progression in any key.

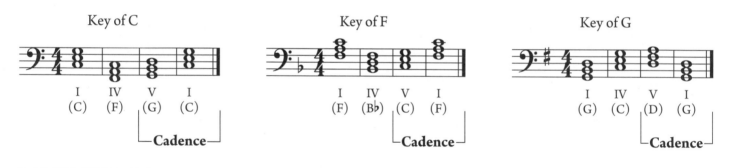

STUDENT ASSIGNMENT

1. Using whole notes, construct the triads in each staff for the common chord progression provided. Name the key.

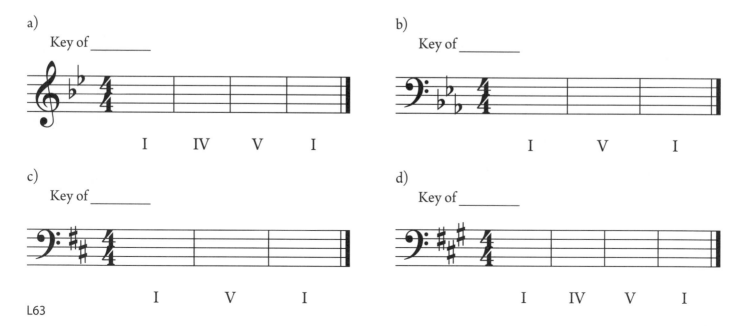

Harmonizing Melodies with
Common Chord Progressions in Major Keys

When applying a chord progression to an existing melody, there are two basic points to consider: 1) How often will the chord change? 2) Which chord "fits" best with the given notes in the melody?

As chords are a foundation, it is often sensible to not change chords very often. As we begin to study this concept, it is helpful to limit the chord selection to one chord per measure.

Merrily We Roll Along (Key of C Major)   Traditional

Chords: I — I — V — I — I — I — V — I

Chord progressions typically start with a I chord. The melody notes E and C indicate this chord will "fit."	With an E in the melody, the best chord choice (I, IV, or V) is **I**.	With a D in the melody, the best chord choice (I, IV, or V) is **V**.	With an E and G in the melody, the best chord choice (I, IV, or V) is **I**.	see measure 1	see measure 2	With three Ds in the melody, as well as beat 1 having a D, the best choice is a **V**.	With a C, this chord could be I or IV. Knowing common chord progressions and the need to cadence, the best choice is **I**.

Progression   I ⟶ V ⟶ I ⟶ V ⟶ I

STUDENT ASSIGNMENT

1. Using only the chords I and V, harmonize the following melody. Circle the notes that fit the chord. Be sure to cadence at the end. It may be helpful to write the note names of the applicable chords for this key in the margins.

Key of _____

Chord Numeral: I   ___ ___ ___ ___ ___ ___ ___

Chord Name: ___ ___ ___ ___ ___ ___ ___ ___

2. Using only the chords I, IV, and V, harmonize the following melody. Circle the notes that fit the chord.

Key of _____

Chord Numeral: I   ___ ___ ___ ___ ___ ___ ___

Chord Name: ___ ___ ___ ___ ___ ___ ___ ___

3. Using only the chords I, IV, and V, harmonize the following melody. Circle the notes that fit the chord.

Key of _____

Chord Numeral: I   ___ ___ ___ ___ ___

Chord Name: ___ ___ ___ ___ ___ ___

Using Chord Progressions in Major Keys

The basic chord progressions you have learned thus far (I–V–I; I–IV–V–I) can be expanded to include additional chords. Over time, progressions have been developed that are considered "pleasing" or "comfortable" to listeners. These progressions are used frequently by composers, but with different melodies and styles. Many of the most popular songs of any time period use these common chord progressions as their musical DNA.

Tips for chord progressions:

I can go to any chord

ii → V is usually as strong as IV → V

V can move to I, IV can move to I, and V can move to vi.

Very common chord progression:

$$I \rightarrow vi \rightarrow \begin{matrix} ii \\ or \\ IV \end{matrix} \rightarrow V \rightarrow I$$

This chord progression moves from left to right. Using cadences allows a composer to get back to the beginning of the progression. V to I is a strong cadence, IV to I is also a cadence commonly used. One additional common choice, though used sparingly per composition, is V to vi.

Common cadences:

V → I   IV → I   V → vi

Experiment with the many possibilities through these basic chord progressions using a piano or guitar. Be sure to finish your musical ideas with one of the common cadences.

STUDENT ASSIGNMENT

1. Harmonize the melody below using I, ii, IV, V, and/or vi. When selecting chords, a) Be sure the melody has notes that fit in the chord. b) Be sure you are moving from left to right in the chord progressions learned. c) Be sure you use one of the common cadences to move to the right in the chord progression. It may be helpful to write the note names of the applicable chords for this key in the margins.

Write the roman numeral and chord names in the spaces provided. Circle the melody notes that fit in the chord.

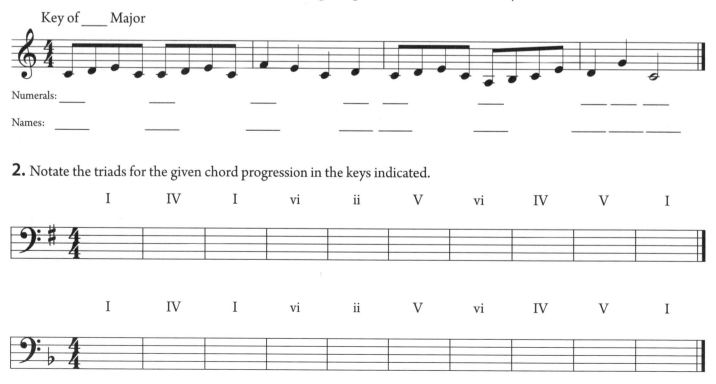

2. Notate the triads for the given chord progression in the keys indicated.

Common Chord Progressions & Melody Harmonization—Working in Minor

Chord progressions in minor follow the same principles as in major. The destination of the journey is **i**. To create a strong cadence, a major **V** is used. This uses the raised seventh scale degree from the harmonic minor scale.

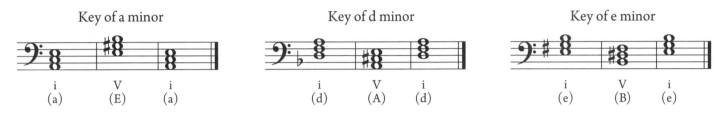

On the journey to the cadence, a common approach to the V chord is the **iv**, just as in major.

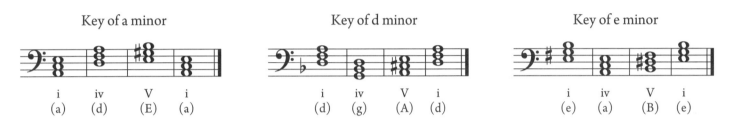

STUDENT ASSIGNMENT

1. Using only the chords i and V, harmonize the following melody. Circle the notes that fit the chord. Be sure to cadence at the end. It may be helpful to write the note names of the applicable chords for this key in the margins.

Key of ____ minor

Chord Numeral: __i__ ____ ____ ____ ____ ____ ____ ____

Chord Name: ____ ____ ____ ____ ____ ____ ____ ____

2. Using only the chords i, iv, and V, harmonize the following melody. Circle the notes that fit the chord.

Key of ____ minor

Chord Numeral: __i__ ____ ____ ____

Chord Name: ____ ____ ____ ____

3. Using only the chords i, iv, and V, harmonize the following melody. Circle the notes that fit the chord.

Key of ____ minor

Chord Numeral: __i__ ____ ____ ____ ____ ____ ____

Chord Name: ____ ____ ____ ____ ____ ____ ____

Harmonizing Major & Minor Melodies Review

Major Keys

1. Using only <u>I</u> and <u>V</u>, harmonize the following melody by writing the roman numerals and chord names in the spaces provided. Circle the notes in the melody that fit in the chord. It may be helpful to write the note names of the applicable chords for this key in the margins.

    Key of ____ Major

Alouette   French Canadian Folk Song

Numerals:

Names:

2. Using only <u>I</u>, <u>IV</u>, and <u>V</u>, harmonize the following melody by writing the roman numerals and chord names in the spaces provided. Circle the notes in the melody that fit in the chord.

    Key of ____ Major

Numerals:

Names:

3. Using <u>I</u>, <u>ii</u>, <u>IV</u>, <u>V</u>, or <u>vi</u>, harmonize the following melody by writing the roman numerals and chord names in the spaces provided. Circle the notes in the melody that fit in the chord.

    Key of ____ Major

Numerals:

Names:

Minor Keys

Using the common minor chord progressions learned (i→V→i, i→iv→V→i), harmonize the following melodies by writing the roman numerals and chord names in the spaces provided. Circle the notes in the melody that fit in the chord.

1.   Key of ____ minor

Numerals:

Names:

2.   Key of ____ minor

Numerals:

Names:

3.   Key of ____ minor

Numerals:

Names:

The Dominant Seventh Chord

As previously learned, a triad is composed of a root, 3rd, and 5th. A **Seventh Chord** is composed of a root, 3rd, 5th, and 7th. A **Dominant Chord** is a triad built off the fifth scale degree (a.k.a. a V chord). Therefore, a **Dominant Seventh Chord** is a seventh chord built off the fifth scale degree in a given key. It is abbreviated as V⁷. While any chord can be made a seventh chord, it is important in our study of chord progressions to focus only on the dominant seventh.

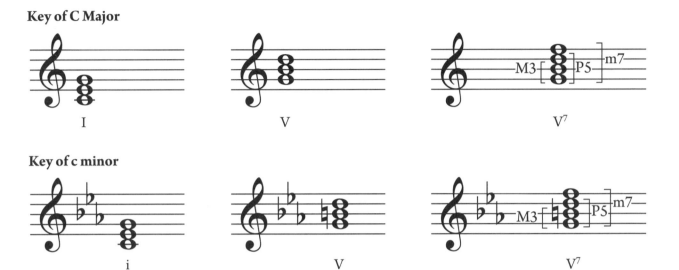

STUDENT ASSIGNMENT

1. Notate I and V⁷ (dominant seventh) chords in each <u>major</u> key indicated.

2. Notate i and V⁷ (dominant seventh) chords in each <u>minor</u> key indicated.

Harmonizing Melodies Using the Dominant Seventh

A dominant seventh chord can be used instead of a V chord in any chord progression.

Because a dominant seventh chord has four notes instead of the three notes of a V chord, it can be used to fit more notes of a melody than the V chord can. For example, the following widely known melody can be harmonized either way:

STUDENT ASSIGNMENT

1. Harmonize each of the indicated major melodies using I, IV, or V⁷. Write the roman numerals and chord names in the spaces provided. Circle the notes of the melody that fit in the chord. It may be helpful to write the note names of the applicable chords for this key in the margins.

2. Harmonize the indicated minor melody using i, iv, or V⁷. Write the roman numerals and chord names in the spaces provided. Circle the notes of the melody that fit in the chord.

Harmonizing Melodies Using Dominant Sevenths Review

Major Keys

1. Using I, ii, IV, V^7, and vi, harmonize each of the indicated major melodies by writing the roman numerals and chord names in the spaces provided. Circle the notes in the melody that fit in the chord. It may be helpful to write the note names of the applicable chords for this key in the margins.

a) Key: ____Major

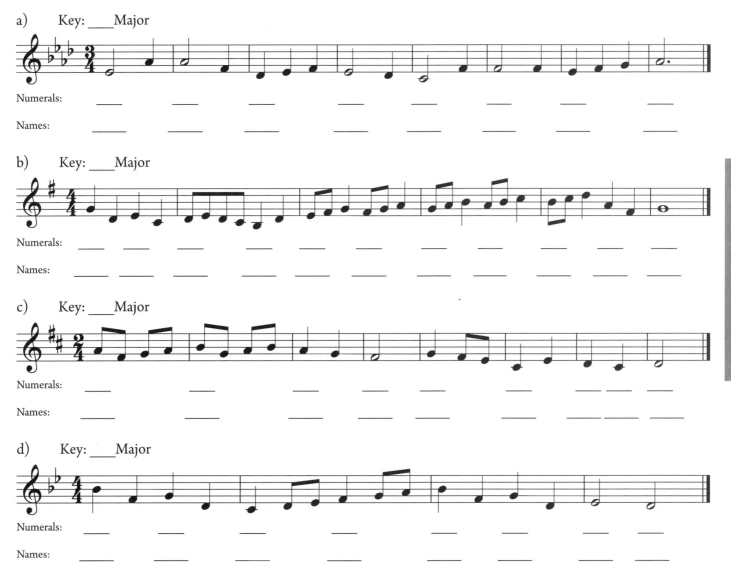

Numerals: ____ ____ ____ ____ ____ ____ ____ ____ ____

Names: ____ ____ ____ ____ ____ ____ ____ ____ ____

b) Key: ____Major

Numerals: ____ ____ ____ ____ ____ ____ ____ ____

Names: ____ ____ ____ ____ ____ ____ ____ ____

c) Key: ____Major

Numerals: ____ ____ ____ ____ ____ ____ ____ ____

Names: ____ ____ ____ ____ ____ ____ ____ ____

d) Key: ____Major

Numerals: ____ ____ ____ ____ ____ ____ ____

Names: ____ ____ ____ ____ ____ ____ ____

Minor Keys

2. Using i, iv, and V^7, harmonize each of the indicated minor melodies by writing the roman numerals and chord names in the spaces provided. Circle the notes in the melody that fit in the chord.

a) Key: ____minor

Numerals: ____ ____ ____ ____ ____ ____

Names: ____ ____ ____ ____ ____ ____

b) Key: ____minor

Numerals: ____ ____ ____ ____ ____ ____

Names: ____ ____ ____ ____ ____ ____

Ear Training Part 15

Audio files can be found in the **Kjos Multimedia Library** at www.kjos.com.

Listen to the following chord progressions.

$$I–V–I \qquad I–V^7–I$$

1. Listen to each chord progression performed. Circle the one you hear in each example.

a) I–V–I   I–V⁷–I

b) I–V–I   I–V⁷–I

c) I–V–I   I–V⁷–I

d) I–V–I   I–V⁷–I

Listen to the following chord progressions.

$$I–IV–V–I \qquad I–IV–V^7–I$$

2. Listen to each chord progression performed. Circle the one you hear in each example.

a) I–IV–V–I   I–IV–V⁷–I

b) I–IV–V–I   I–IV–V⁷–I

c) I–IV–V–I   I–IV–V⁷–I

d) I–IV–V–I   I–IV–V⁷–I

Listen to the following chord progressions.

$$i–V–i \qquad i–V^7–i$$

3. Listen to each chord progression performed. Circle the one you hear in each example.

a) i–V–i   i–V⁷–i

b) i–V–i   i–V⁷–i

c) i–V–i   i–V⁷–i

d) i–V–i   i–V⁷–i

Listen to the following chord progressions.

$$i–iv–V–i \qquad i–iv–V^7–i$$

4. Listen to each chord progression performed. Circle the one you hear in each example.

a) i–iv–V–i   i–iv–V⁷–i

b) i–iv–V–i   i–iv–V⁷–i

c) i–iv–V–i   i–iv–V⁷–i

d) i–iv–V–i   i–iv–V⁷–i

Listen to the following chord progressions.

$$I–vi–IV–V^7–I \qquad I–vi–ii–V^7–I$$

5. Listen to each chord progression performed. Circle the one you hear in each example.

a) I–vi–IV–V⁷–I   I–vi–ii–V⁷–I

b) I–vi–IV–V⁷–I   I–vi–ii–V⁷–I

c) I–vi–IV–V⁷–I   I–vi–ii–V⁷–I

d) I–vi–IV–V⁷–I   I–vi–ii–V⁷–I

Composing a Melody

There is no formula when composing a melody; however, all of the music theory learned thus far can be of help. For some composers, the melody comes first and the harmony second—much like the previous exercises. For others, a melody is drawn from a chord progression. It is the latter method that will be explored here.

When writing a melody, there are many decisions to be made. For example, the composer will need to decide: a) what instrument or voice will perform the melody; b) what key will the melody will be in; c) what time signature will be used to capture the feeling to be portrayed by the melody; e) how "singable" the melody will be (e.g., does the melody limit the number of large intervallic skips and include stepwise motion?). Once you have the setting of the music prepared (e.g., $\frac{4}{4}$ time, key of C Major, *moderato, mezzo forte*, using I–vi–ii–V^7–I over four measures), sketch where the chord changes will occur, as well as which tones are chord tones on the staff as a reference. See below:

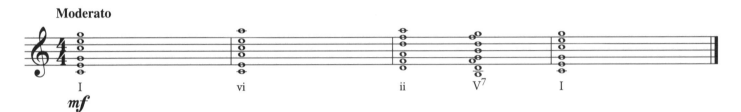

As you write the melody line from chord to chord, you may want to use notes that do not "fit" in the chord. These pitches are called *non-chord tones*. The notes can be found easily in the previous exercises as they are the melody notes that remained un-circled. Many times, these non-chord tones occur on weaker beats in the measure (e.g., 2 and 4 in $\frac{4}{4}$ time) or in between beats in the measure (such as on the second eighth note in a pair of eighth notes). Including some non-chord tones in your melodies will create more interesting and flexible lines.

A final suggestion is to look at the chord tones that are shared from chord to chord. In our current example, when moving from I to vi, the tones C and E are shared among those chords. Using those notes in both chords could be interesting, and result in a very "singable" melody. See an example below:

In the above melody, the non-chord tones are circled. In $\frac{4}{4}$ time, beats 1 and 3 are considered strong beats, while 2 and 4 are considered weak beats. Notice in this example how the non-chord tones occur on beats 2 and 4. Also, take note that the largest skip in the melody is a third, and that there is frequent use of stepwise motion. Of further interest is the similar rhythmic figure used in measures 1 and 3. This rhythm, being familiar from measure 1, then makes the melody seem familiar in measure 3, even though it is new.

In the end, the composer will decide what he or she feels works best. Using the common chord progressions and cadences learned thus far may guide you to create a successful melody.

Listen to your favorite music. Listen to what chords are used. Listen to the shape of the melodies you hear. Use what you like in your writing, and do not be fearful of making mistakes.

STUDENT ASSIGNMENT—Composing a Melody

1. Write a four-bar melody to fit the indicated progression. Circle the non-chord tones.

a)

b)

3. a) Choose a <u>major</u> key.   b) Choose a time signature.   c) Choose a tempo.   d) Select chords based on common progressions.   e) Sketch the chord tones over the changes.   f) Write a melody.   g) Circle the non-chord tones.

4. a) Choose a <u>minor</u> key.   b) Choose a time signature.   c) Choose a tempo.   d) Select chords based on common progressions.   e) Sketch the chord tones over the changes.   f) Write a melody.   g) Circle the non-chord tones.

5. Write an <u>eight-measure</u> melody in a key, time signature, and tempo of your choice Be sure to indicate chord changes using roman numerals, and circle all non-chord tones.

The Middle Ages (400–1400 C.E.)

SIGNS OF THE TIMES (History and Culture)

The Romanesque Period of the Middle Ages (500–1100) is a fascinating era for study in the modern age. Many present day influences, institutions, and inventions had their birth during this era. The fact that this period is also the connective link between ancient history (Ancient Rome, Ancient Greece, etc.) and modern times (Northern Europe, Russia, the Americas, etc.) flavors its study with an understanding of the rise and fall of civilizations. The Romanesque Period contained many great personalities who contributed much to what influences our culture even today. Included in these were St. Augustine (d. 604), who was the first Archbishop of Canterbury; St. Francis of Assisi (1181–1226); and Dante Alighieri, often considered the father of the Italian language. These men and others contributed to history and culture with their writings, inventions, humanitarianism, art, and music.

The feudal system of government and class structure arose during this time and was primarily controlled by the Catholic Church. Social class structure was basically distilled down to three classes of people—the Church (clergy), the ruling classes (consisting of lords who ruled over large blocks of land), and the serfs (or peasants, who lived in poverty and worked the land for the feudal lords). After his coronation on Christmas Day in 800, Charlemagne's court in Aachen was considered the hub of European cultural revival.

The Gothic Period (1100–1500) saw a lessening of the Church's political power. The Crusades began in 1096 and brought with them an unexpected influence in the culture. Knights from all over Europe marched to the Holy Land in order to fight and remove the Muslim Turks and other non-Christian sects residing in Israel. These knights brought back to their homes Middle Eastern influences such as social customs, entertainment, and a sense of more independence. The impact of the Crusades, particularly at the political and social levels, can still be seen today. The Gothic Era also saw much more development of roads and towns in Northern Europe.

ARTISTIC PURPOSE

Very little is known about music produced in the Romanesque Period, due to a lack of a systematic way of notating music. Some early examples of music maintained by the Catholic Church are available today; however, without the benefit of organized written music, it is hard to recreate an authentic version of the music. Music's function revolved around the church setting and was included in all church rituals from Mass to Lauds (early morning recitations) and Vespers (evening prayer service). During the Gothic Period, music and art took on an increasingly important role. Nobility became patrons of more secular music in everyday language. This led to more prominence of the individual musician/composer which in turn led to a more pressing need for a standardized system of notating music.

CREATIVE CHARACTERISTICS

Although secular music in the Romanesque Period existed, very little of it was preserved because there were no institutions in place to keep any traditions outside of the church. Traveling performers such as jongleurs and minstrels performed songs both instrumentally and vocally, danced, juggled, and performed tricks for the entertainment of nobility and common people alike. Music with instruments was generally banned in the church. Vocal music continued to be the accepted form of music in church worship services. Transitioning into the Gothic Age, music continued to display more organization from a rhythmic, notational, and harmonic standpoint. Most of the melody lines, particularly in secular pieces, followed a form that rose and fell with the lyrical structure of the verse.

INSTRUMENT UPDATE

The Medieval instrumental ensembles were classified in two different ways, as either "loud" or "soft." The loud ensembles contained instruments that were predominantly the precursors to the brass family of instruments today, including the trumpet, trombone, shawm, horn, and bagpipe. Soft ensembles primarily used flutes, recorders, lutes, and keyboards.

The Middle Ages (400–1400 C.E.)

400 C.E.   600   800   1000   1200   1400

1. Place these historical events at the correct place on the timeline by inserting a vertical line and the corresponding letter.

   a. Charlemagne begins his systematic territorial expansion, which ultimately unifies a large portion of Europe (774)

   b. The original London Bridge, which is made of wood, falls when the Saxons pull it down (1014)

   c. Geoffrey Chaucer (1334–1400) probably writes The Canterbury Tales between 1382 and 1400

2. Why is there very little known about music produced in the Romanesque Period?

   There was not much of a system for notating music.

3. In which period of the Middle Ages did more secular music exist?

   Gothic Period

4. a) List four examples of the types of instruments used in loud ensembles.

   Trumpet, Trombone, horn, bag pipe

   b) List four examples of the types of instruments used in soft ensembles.

   Flutes, recorder, keyboard, lute

5. Fill in the letter of the description that best matches each word or phrase.

   _*b*_ jongleurs and minstrels   a. church rituals that involved music

   _*a*_ Mass, Lauds, and Vespers   b. traveling performers

   _*c*_ clergy, ruling classes, and serfs or peasants   c. social classes of people in the feudal system of government

The Renaissance (1400–1600 C.E.)

SIGNS OF THE TIMES (History and Culture)

Though it contained a number of political and social upheavals, the Renaissance Period is known more for its cultural movement and scientific developments. Many scientific and technical advances we typically attribute to the 20th century actually had their initial birth in the Renaissance. Leonardo da Vinci designed a helicopter, a tank, and a calculator, and he developed a theory for plate tectonics. The Renaissance held many other scientific minds of advanced thinking. Copernicus and Galileo both made many discoveries in the field of astronomy and posed new theories that were proven true centuries later.

Science and art frequently blended together as excellence in these disciplines was reached by the great minds of the period such as da Vinci, Michelangelo, and Vesalius. Much of this blending of science and art came in the advancing studies in anatomy. Perhaps the most significant aspect of these scientific and cultural developments came not so much in the findings themselves, but rather in the process by which they came. In other words, men were thinking about everything in new and different ways, and this led to significant advancements in many areas.

ARTISTIC PURPOSE

With the transition of music from being solely available through the Church to also being available in aristoractic households, it in turn evolved from passive entertainment into active participation. The madrigal and chanson forms reflected emotional intimacy with their vernacular text (everyday language) and themes/subject matters of love, unsatisfied desire, humor, satire, and politics.

Toward the end of the Renaissance, instrumental music became very popular among the aristocracy as a form of entertainment. This music was presented by professional musicians and skilled amateurs and typically took place in the homes of nobility and the wealthy. Formal court functions also began to hold more prominence, and in response, composers began to write dances for these occasions.

Church music also underwent changes, particularly relative to the Protestant Reformation. The newly formed Lutheran Church broke away from the standard sacred forms used by the Catholic Church, instead embracing more simplistic music that incorporated folk music heritage of the common people of the congregation.

CREATIVE CHARACTERISTICS

Renaissance music continued to progress throughout the era as composers began incorporating less restrictive rhythms and harmonies. Compositions continued to be based on a tonal center; however, the tonal organization was not so much of a vertical harmonic structure. Rather, the tonal relationships were more linear. With this focus on organizing melody based on interval relationships, harmonic texture began to find its way into music in the sixteenth century. Another important organizational method in Renaissance music was the use of repetition and contrast. Josquin des Prez's (c. 1440–1521) motet, *Ave Maria,* demonstrates an excellent example of this method.

As with much of Renaissance music, instruments provided underlying accompaniment to a vocal melody line. However, all exclusively instrumental music was based on dances and performed with either a solo instrument or a small instrumental ensemble. The lute was the most widely used instrument during this era, holding much the same position as the piano would in the 19th century.

INSTRUMENT UPDATE

Music was a very important component to the success of theatrical productions. Though information regarding this type of music is limited, it would appear that a typical theater band might consist of eight to twelve players and include cornets, hautbois, recorders, a few brass instruments, drums, and sometimes a few strings. Vocal music for the theater included ballads and popular songs, as Shakespeare frequently exampled.

Military music also took on a new role during the Renaissance with the wind band becoming essential in communication, as trumpets, flutes, and drums were used to send signals from one portion of an army to another.

The Renaissance (1400–1600 C.E.)

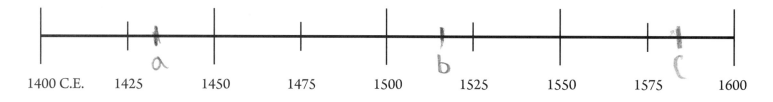

1400 C.E.   1425   1450   1475   1500   1525   1550   1575   1600

1. Place these historical events at the correct place on the timeline by inserting a vertical line and the corresponding letter.

   a. Joan of Arc is burned at the stake (1431)

   b. Martin Luther initiates the Protestant Reformation by posting his 95 Theses (October 31, 1517)

   c. Pope Gregory XIII adopts the Gregorian Calendar, which fixes the vernal equinox on March 21 (1582)

2. In what way did instrumental music become very popular toward the end of the Renaissance?

   As a form of entertainment

3. How did Renaissance composers respond to the more prominent formal court functions?

   Composers wrote dances

4. Name two ways instruments were used in Renaissance music.

   ① accompaniment to vocal melody

   ② ?

5. Which instrument was the most widely used during this era?

   lute

6. Name three instruments that might be included in a theater band during the Renaissance.

   recorder, drums, string instruments

7. How were trumpets, flutes, and drums used in the Renaissance Era military?

   to send signals

8. Fill in the letter of the description that best matches each word or phrase.

   __C__ madrigal and chanson

   __a__ repetition and contrast

   __b__ harmonic texture

   a. type of musical organization method demonstrated in *Ave Maria*, by Josquin des Prez

   b. method of organizing melody based on interval relationships

   c. forms of music that reflected emotional intimacy, love, unsatisfied desire, humor, satire, and politics

The Baroque Period (1600–1750 C.E.)

SIGNS OF THE TIMES (History and Culture)

The 17th century marked many changes at multiple levels, particularly in Europe and the Americas—the Protestant Reformation, with the rising merchant/capitalism economic system, the rise of monarchy forms of government, and significant scientific developments and discoveries. All these elements blended into the growth of the new attitude or spirit being reflected in the Baroque cultural movement. The most identifying characteristics of the Baroque Period were the interesting combination of strong energy and strong emotion paired with the use of imagery and subtlety. Music resonated with new melody structure, harmony, and texture.

The development of music during the Baroque Era was not merely limited to the differences between religious and secular music. A secondary line of growth occurred with vocal music and its new forms of opera, oratorio, and the cantata. Instrumental music took on a new role apart from the primary use as accompaniment for vocal performances. This expansion in the application and appreciation of instrumental music performance led to its prominence over other musical art forms by the end of this period.

ARTISTIC PURPOSE

Just as in the earlier part of the Baroque Period, the latter half (the beginning of the 18th century) categorized its music by its use—theater, church, or chamber music. During this time, composers turned to a more personal emotional expression, illustrating a wide variety of sentiments.

Opera, a new form of composition developed in the 17th century, combined every artistic form available, including both vocal and instrumental music, art, architecture, and literature. Opera evolved from a desire to revive the ideals of classic antiquity that began in the Renaissance. Born in Italy, the early operas immediately began using a new style of music—the recitative, or musically reciting of the text (or libretto) of the drama. Recitatives were mingled with arias, melodic songs which were very expressive and frequently written to highlight the vocal skills of the performer. The recitative's purpose was to tell what was happening in the story; the aria's purpose was to comment on the story's events.

Another new phenomenon during these years was the gradual development of the orchestra into a form much as we see it today. The backbone of the Baroque orchestra was the string choir (or section), and though the orchestra contained woodwinds and brass instruments, the distinction of separate sections would not yet occur until the latter half of the 18th century.

CREATIVE CHARACTERISTICS

As stated previously, music of the Baroque Era was very emotionally charged and expressed a very personal side of the composer. In order to achieve this expressive nature of the music, the use of dissonance and chromatic styles became widely used. Arbitrary and changing rhythms also created a whimsical mood. Dynamics became very important to the expressiveness of the music. Performers played a greater creative role as they were allowed more leeway to improvise and ornament on the written notes as long as they used good taste and judgment.

Harmonic style grew as major and minor harmonies developed out of a tonal center with a strong bass line supporting the harmonies above. This bass line, marked to indicate harmonies to be played with each note, was known as the "figured bass" and became a strong, primary characteristic in Baroque music.

INSTRUMENT UPDATE

Throughout the Baroque Period, instruments continued to develop and evolve, allowing for a player to achieve new and better results in tone, range, keys, etc. The horn was one instrument that underwent significant changes during the 17th century, growing in lengths up to twelve feet. The shape of the horn also changed from a multi-coil style to an open hoop shape, allowing the player to change key centers when needed by using different sized crooks or tubing extentions.

The Baroque Period (1600–1750 C.E.)

1600 C.E.   1625   1650   1675   1700   1725   1750

1. Place these historical events at the correct place on the timeline by inserting a vertical line and the corresponding letter.
   a. St. Peter's Basilica in the Vatican is completed (1626)
   b. Harvard University is founded in Boston, Massachusetts (1636)
   c. The City of New Orleans is founded by the French in North America (1718)

2. Which type of music became most prominent by the end of the Baroque Period?

   Instrumental music

3. Name three categories of Baroque music defined by the type of use.

   Opera, oratoria, cantata — *theather, church, chamber*

4. Which new form of composition combined every artistic form available in the Baroque Period?

   Opera

5. Name two ways that a more expressive nature was achieved in Baroque style.

   dissonance & chromatic styles

6. The Baroque Period saw the distinction of separate sections of the orchestra.

   ☑ True   ☐ False

7. Name one instrument that changed significantly during the 17th century.

   Horn

8. Fill in the letter of the description that best matches each word or phrase.

   b recitative   a. expressive, melodic song written to highlight a performer's vocal skills

   d libretto   b. musically reciting the text of an opera drama

   c figured bass   c. musical line marked to indicate harmonies to be played with each note

   a aria   d. text of an opera

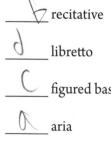

The Classical Period (1750–1820 C.E.)

SIGNS OF THE TIMES (History and Culture)

The 18th century was an interesting dichotomy of systemized, formalized intellectual processes in the cultural influences of the times—politics, religion, industry, art, music, and literature—juxtaposed with an age of revolution beginning with the American Revolution and climaxing with the French Revolution. At some level, this dichotomy was seen specifically in the music of the times, as composers began embracing more and more structure in their music forms while seeking to break free from the highly ornamental, emotional music of the Baroque Period. Many small courts of nobility and aristocracy that formed the primary base of patronage for musicians and artists sought to maintain their status and position through the arts and social standing rather than through political and economic influences.

Several significant developments in the world of music took place during the Classical Period from a social and a business standpoint. Music became a much more international venture with publication and touring rapidly growing, crossing borders and oceans. Concert societies became very fashionable venues for the promotion of particular composers or styles of music. Another development of this period came with the introduction of folk music and its themes into serious music. This was most likely due to the wide class range of the 18th century audience. With the increase in venues for public concerts, musical entertainment was available to almost every class of people. This and the fact that music was the primary form of entertainment caused composers to turn their attention to themes that would ring familiar to their audiences.

ARTISTIC PURPOSE

Music saw several significant changes during this period, particularly at an instrumental level. The structure of the orchestra changed, increasing in size and range. More important than these basic changes, however, was a shift in the way pieces were orchestrated and the way instruments were used. This new orchestration technique created clear divisions as to which instruments became devoted to melody and which would carry the supporting harmonies. Subdivisions between the various instrumental choirs were also born in this time, such as Violin I and Violin II, Trumpet I and II, etc.

Vocal music continued to progress through opera, oratorios, and choruses. Great importance was given to these forms and they gained the most popularity among the people who loved the elegant spectacle of theatrical music. Music for dancing also became increasingly popular as the aristocratic society pursued their love of gaiety and entertainment.

CREATIVE CHARACTERISTICS

The clean, symmetrical forms of the Classical Period created a very simple texture to the music, which allowed for a greater demonstration of dynamic and phrasing expression. While simplicity was important to composers of this era, variety was equally important. Diversity in the use of keys, rhythms, moods, and timbres characterized music of the Classical Period as composers strove to achieve dramatic results. Also, with the simplification of overall texture, detail became more important and allowed for rhythmic nuances such as opening fanfares, funeral march rhythms, or minuet form. These details also assisted in providing the unifying tone of a given movement.

Form structure also became more defined as the era progressed. *Concerto grosso* (concerto for more than one musician) was slowly evolving into the more popular solo concerto (concerto featuring only one soloist). The most well-known composers of the day—Haydn, Mozart, Gluck, and Beethoven—all contributed to the development of the style that is most clearly identified as that of the Classical Period.

INSTRUMENT UPDATE

Military bands continued to evolve during the Classical Period, as two different types of groups developed. One style of band was very much like the popular *Harmonie* groups, consisting of eight instruments and frequently performing *Harmoniemusik*. The second type of band included the basic octet along with some Turkish instrumentation that included heavy brass, percussion, and piccolos.

The Classical Period (1750–1820 C.E.)

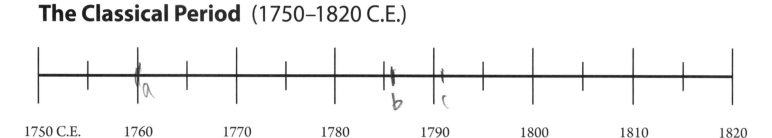

1750 C.E.   1760   1770   1780   1790   1800   1810   1820

1. Place these historical events at the correct place on the timeline by inserting a vertical line and the corresponding letter.

    a. Catherine the Great becomes ruler of Russia (1760)

    b. Mozart's opera, *The Marriage of Figaro*, premiers in Vienna (May 1, 1786)

    c. The *Old Farmers Almanac* is first published (1792)

2. How did the structure of the orchestra change during the Classical Period?

   - increased in size & range
   - shift in how pieces were orchestrated and how instruments were used.

3. Which vocal forms continued to progress and gain popularity during the Classical Period?

   Opera, oratorios, ~~cantatas~~ Choruses

4. Name four well-known Classical composers.

   Haydn, Mozart, Gluck, Beethoven

5. Fill in the letter of the description that best matches each word or phrase.

   _*d*_ concerto grosso

   _*a*_ solo concerto

   _*b*_ fanfares, funeral march rhythms, and minuet form

   _*c*_ diverse use of keys, rhythms, moods, and timbres

   a. concerto for only one soloist

   b. examples of rhythmic nuances allowed by the simplification of overall texture

   c. characterized Classical music

   d. concerto for more than one musician

The Romantic Period (1820–1900 C.E.)

SIGNS OF THE TIMES (History and Culture)

With the pursuit of personal expression being the primary motivation in art and music during the Romantic Period, identification of an artist or composer became much easier based upon their work. Greater emphasis on national loyalties and ties was on the rise and consequently this too became reflected in the arts. Many composers began conveying a sense of nationalism in their music through greater use of folk music, legendary historical subject matter, dance, and overall native cultural flavor. This regional/cultural texture also made composer recognition easier. Composers such as Beethoven, Wagner, Schubert, Liszt, and many others were all popular entertainment figures of their day because each of their individual styles of music contained all the elements necessary to make them easily identifiable both from a practical and emotional standpoint. In fact, Beethoven was one of the first composers to successfully work completely independently of an aristocratic patron.

The extreme disparity between the social classes leveled out considerably in the 19th century and consequently composers' work was directed primarily toward the middle class. As public concerts and theatrical presentations were the primary form of entertainment, audiences sought relief from their everyday lives through the emotionally charged music of this period.

ARTISTIC PURPOSE

Another development seen in music during the Romantic Period was the rise of the virtuoso artist. The drive to create intense, free-formed, emotionally-charged music meant that composers wrote increasingly technical music that also included a great deal of improvisation. This improvisation is what lent a sense of intimacy to the excellent technical skills that, in turn, made the virtuoso performance so enjoyable. In particular, the virtuoso piano and violin recitals became very popular, having been pioneered by Niccolò Paganini, the famous violin virtuoso.

The other area of greatest development in the world of music came with the striking increase in music education and teaching venues. Composers and musicians now had more opportunities to earn a reliable living with their craft both through performance and through teaching. Some of the most famous present-day conservatories were founded during this time.

CREATIVE CHARACTERISTICS

Music created during the Romantic Period is probably more distinguishable to even the untrained ear than any other period that preceded it. This is, in part, due to the unique sound and texture combined with expanded forms, melodic themes, and greater technical skills. The growth of the traditional orchestra, both in section structure and in instrument advancement, led to the ability to present dramatic symphonies, concert overtures, and other programme music. The denser, weightier textures being developed provided a dramatic backdrop for lyrical melodies and richer harmonies. Simple melodic themes were developed through recurring variations, giving shape and unity to a multi-movement piece. Chromaticism and discord were frequent choices to focus the ebb and flow of climaxes throughout a piece of music, and they created an interesting, opposing harmonic canvas on which to lay the lyrical melodies so favored during this period.

INSTRUMENT UPDATE

One of the most interesting aspects of instrumental music in the Romantic Period was the growth in popularity of the concert band. French, English, and Prussian (German) wind ensembles had been gaining interest and appreciation since the Classical Period, particularly with the *Harmonie* ensemble movement throughout Europe. However, full orchestra and theatrical performances such as opera and ballet had been the mainstay of entertainment for several centuries. By the mid-19th century, the small wind ensemble had grown to include more members, more varied instrumentation, and more diverse composition options.

The Romantic Period (1820–1900 C.E.)

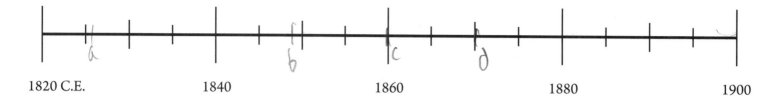

1820 C.E.   1840   1860   1880   1900

1. Place these historical events at the correct place on the timeline by inserting a vertical line and the corresponding letter.

   a. James Fennimore Cooper publishes *The Last of the Mohicans* (1826)

   b. The first gold rush to California begins (1848)

   c. San Francisco, California, is the site of the first baseball game (1860)

   d. Rome becomes the capital of Italy (1870)

2. What was the primary motivation in art and music during the Romantic Period?

   pursuit of personal expression

3. Name four Romantic composers who were easily identifiable because of their individual styles.

   Beethoven, Wagner, liszt, Schubert

4. What was the primary form of entertainment in the 19th century?

   Public concerts & theatrical presentations

5. Name the famous violinist who pioneered virtuoso piano and violin recitals.

   Paganini

6. How is Romantic music more distinguishable from the music of any previous period?

   Due to unique sound & texture combined w/ expanded forms, melodic themes and greater technical scales.

7. What made way for lyrical melodies and richer harmonies in Romantic music?

   denser, weighted textures.

8. The concert band increased in popularity during the Romantic Period.

   ☑ True   ☐ False

The 20th Century

SIGNS OF THE TIMES (History and Culture)

Originality to the point of questionability could be a possible description for the experimental nature of modernistic music in the 20th century. Composers of the contemporary "classical" music of this era were known to revisit previous eras in a new or "neo" way, such as neoclassicism, neoromanticism, and the like. Aleatory music (one type being chance music) demonstrated experimental techniques in the extreme, using elements that would previously have never been considered possible for music. Overall, 20th century music carried an underlying attitude of revolt to all that had come before as composers pursued their desires for extreme expression.

This revolutionary attitude is not surprising when considered beside the innovation that was occurring at the scientific and social levels of the period. The Industrial Age was evolving into the Technological Age, societal influences were shifting from community involvement to self-expression. Consequently, the contemporary composer who abandoned traditional styles in favor of extreme expression typically found himself with only a very limited audience.

ARTISTIC PURPOSE

In a sense, the 20th century turned the life of an everyday world into a constant performance venue. With the development of portable electronic devices in the last half of the century, music became available every moment of every day for nearly every person. While this constant musical "stage" presented significant business and creative opportunities for composers and arrangers, it also had the negative effect of dulling the appreciation senses of the listener and creating a less discerning or cultivated audience.

Perhaps one of the more positive results of music development in this century was the growth of the music programs in the public schools of America. Although the practice of music tutoring carried forward from previous centuries, its purpose changed substantially as music composition and performance were not nearly the financially viable careers they had been during the Romantic Period. With the onset of music programs being included in the education system, more children became exposed to culturally influential aspects of the discipline, as well as new opportunities for employment within the field of music in the form of teachers. In particular, the American school band movement, through events such as the Schools Band Contest of America (first held in 1923), encouraged new stability, standards of performance, and improved literature for young musicians.

CREATIVE CHARACTERISTICS

The driving force of original expression found in 20th century "classical" music certainly eliminated the ability to assign detailed characteristics to the overall period. Typically, the generalized impressions of dissonance and atonality, abnormal instrumentation, and experimental thinking come to mind. However, a few more characteristics can be applied in general to the era. Many composers enjoyed using variations on a theme as a main component of their composition. In addition, these contemporary composers were much more brief and to the point in their delivery, replacing elaborate thematic structure with tightly arranged motive elements. Melody lines reflected more vertical rather than horizontal movement with the use of wide interval skips. In particular, vocal melodies displayed contours that reflected the content of the text. Rhythm also demonstrated a fascination with irregularity through the use of asymmetry and simultaneous rhythmic occurrences.

INSTRUMENT UPDATE

By the early 20th century, orchestral and wind ensemble instrumentation had been firmly established for a number of decades. Few changes or improvements to the mechanics of traditional instruments were occurring. However, the electronic movement began to develop instruments outside the expected electric guitar or piano. The electronic wind instrument and the electronic valve instrument were created, and these simulate sounds of any number of instruments while avoiding tuning and projection issues. Vocal music was also impacted by the electronic movement as innovators sought to try to reproduce the human voice electronically with synthesizers and later with computers. As the 20th century closed, orchestral, wind ensemble, and choral music all saw a melding of the traditional and the electronic instrumentation in both professional and amateur settings. It will be interesting to see what the future holds for the continuing evolution of music.

The 20th Century

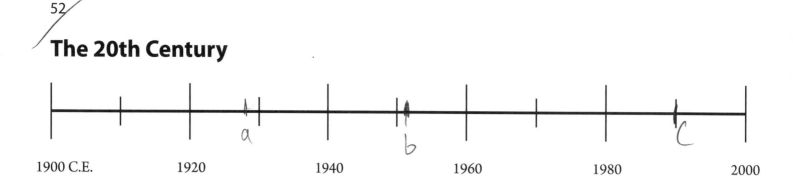

1900 C.E. 1920 1940 1960 1980 2000

1. Place these historical events at the correct place on the timeline by inserting a vertical line and the corresponding letter.

   a. In a test that becomes contaminated, Alexander Fleming discovers penicillin (1928)

   b. Princess Elizabeth becomes Queen Elizabeth II of England (1952)

   c. Lech Walesa becomes the first elected president of Poland (1990)

2. What does the prefix *neo-* (e.g., neoclassicism or neoromanticism) mean?

   new

3. a) What made music more available every moment of every day for nearly every person in the last half of the 20th century?

   Portable music devices

   b) In what way did this extreme increase in availability have a negative effect?

   Dulling appreciation senses of listener & creating less discerning audience.

4. Name three musical aspects the American school band movement encouraged.

   new stability   standards of performance   improved literature

5. Name three generalized impressions that can be used to describe 20th century music.

   dissonance & atonality   experimental thinking   abnormal instrumentation

6. Composers in the 20th century employed more elaborate thematic structure.

   ☐ True   ☑ False

7. What two issues did the development and improvement of electronic instruments avoid?

   tuning and projection issues.

20th Century Pop Music

Jazz

One of the primary characteristics that make jazz music so distinctive is the improvisation aspect of its performance. A skilled jazz musician will individualize and interpret a piece of music, feeling it as he or she goes, and perhaps playing it differently each time.

The 1950s marked a decline in the raging popularity and sheer number of big bands. Those that continued seemed to change with the times, reflecting the influences of bebop, 20th century art music, cool jazz, pop, and rock styles. Buddy Rich (1917–1987), drummer and bandleader, played with a number of groups and in 1966 formed his own very successful big band. Maynard Ferguson (1928–2006), a Canadian-born trumpet player and band leader, played with various big bands and then formed a series of his own beginning in the late 1950s. Ferguson is best known for his facility and endurance in the high register of the trumpet.

Jazz-rock, also sometimes called fusion, combines jazz improvisation and chord progressions with the rhythms of rock. Generally, it is more electronic than acoustic, featuring synthesizer, electric bass, electric guitar, electronically processed woodwind and brass instruments, and a great deal of percussion. Some well-known jazz-rock musicians include Chick Corea (1941–), electric guitarist and composer Pat Metheny (1954–), the group Chicago (initially known as Chicago Transit Authority), and Blood, Sweat, and Tears, which included vocals backed by a rock rhythm section, trombone, trumpet, and saxophone.

Rock

Rock changed dramatically beginning in the 1970s with the use of more electronic instruments, sophisticated recording techniques, and theatrical enhancements in live performances. The 1980s and 1990s saw a changed role for many musicians, as the synthesizer, drum machine, computer, and digital recorder all became important tools in the creation, performance, and recording of popular music. MTV (Music Television), formed in 1982, started as a 24-hour television network that played short videos accompanying rock songs. MTV revolutionized the way popular music was appreciated. Rock also spawned other music styles such as rap, alternative, and heavy metal.

Carole King (1942–), a prolific songwriter, pianist and singer, enjoyed tremendous success with her 1971 album, *Tapestry*. Its distinctive folk-flavored music made this her landmark album, and it was the top-selling pop solo album for eleven years until Michael Jackson's 1982 release, *Thriller*, claimed the spot. Bob Dylan (1941–), another multi-talented singer-songwriter, has also had a long and influential career beginning in the 1960s through present day that was flavored by a number of genres including folk, blues, country, and rock and roll. James Brown (1933–2006) was renowned as one of the greatest entertainers of the 20th century and influenced subsequent generations of performers with his energetic rock/rhythm and blues style. Alicia Keys (1981–), singer-songwriter and pianist, represents a new generation of pop musicians creating music with a unique blend of rhythm and blues, soul, and classical-style piano.

20th Century Pop Music

1. Underline three interesting facts about each style of music on the previous page.

2. What is a distinctive primary characteristic of jazz music?

Improvisation

3. For what skill is Maynard Ferguson best known?

facility & endurance in high registers of trumpet

4. Give another name for jazz-rock.

fusion

5. Name four well-known jazz-rock musicians or groups.

① Chick Corea ② Pat Metheny

③ Blood, Sweat, and tears ④ Chicago

6. Name three ways rock changed dramatically, beginning in the 1970s.

① More electronic instruments
② Sophisticated recording techniques
③ Theatrical enhancements at live performances

7. Explain the basis of MTV.

24 hour TV network that played short videos accompanying Rock songs.

8. Name three music styles that have roots in rock music.

① Rap

② Alternative

③ Heavy Metal

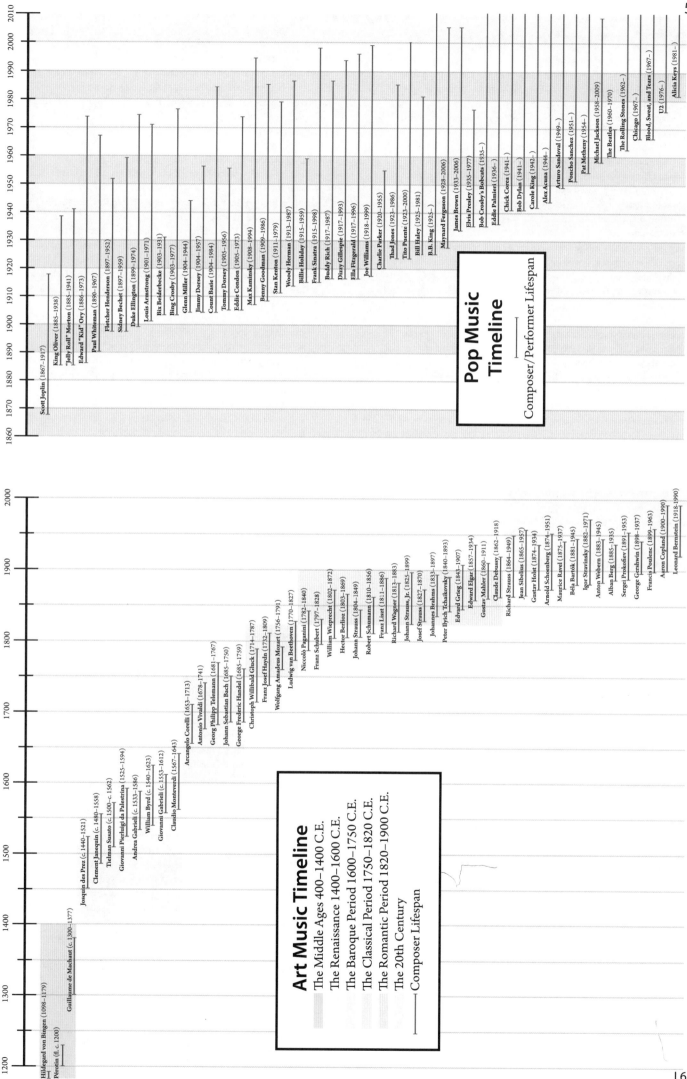

Pop Music Timeline

— Composer/Performer Lifespan

Art Music Timeline

The Middle Ages 400–1400 C.E.
The Renaissance 1400–1600 C.E.
The Baroque Period 1600–1750 C.E.
The Classical Period 1750–1820 C.E.
The Romantic Period 1820–1900 C.E.
The 20th Century
— Composer Lifespan

Glossary

aleatory music – a.k.a. chance music; music that demonstrates experimentation to the extreme

American school band movement – movement that encouraged new stability, standards of performance, and improved literature for young musicians

aria – expressive, melodic song written to highlight a performer's vocal skills

art music – music distinguished from popular music

atonality – use of harmonic structure in music composition that does not create a relationship between dissonance and consonance

augmented interval – interval created when the top note of a major or perfect interval is raised by a half step

augmented triad – triad in which both the top and the bottom thirds are major; major triad with a raised 5th

ballad – narrative form of verse set to music

bebop – 20th century music characterized by more complex melodies and chord progressions as well as more emphasis on the role of the rhythm section

blues – music genre rooted in African-American field hollers, work songs, and spirituals of the rural southern United States, based on sad subjects

cadence – chord progression that marks the end of a phrase of music

cantata – musical form that recognizes and conveys the spirit of a particular event or holiday

chanson – Renaissance musical form that reflected emotional intimacy with vernacular text

chorus – musical ensemble of singers, or music written for such a group

chord progression – series of two or more chords played in succession

chromatic – including notes outside the prevailing key, based on half steps

common time (C) – a.k.a. $\frac{4}{4}$

concert band – a.k.a. wind ensemble; large performance group of wind instruments and percussion

concert overture – single-movement instrumental musical piece, popular in the Romantic Period

concerto grosso – Baroque music form; concerto for more than one musician

conservatory – music school

contemporary classical – genre of music referring to modern art music, rather than music from the Classical Period

cut time (¢) – a.k.a. $\frac{2}{2}$ or *Alla Breve*

diminished interval – interval created when the top note of a minor or perfect interval is lowered by a half step

diminished triad – triad in which both the top and the bottom thirds are minor; minor triad with a lowered 5th

dissonance – use of notes outside the prevailing harmony

dominant chord – triad built off the 5th scale degree (V chord)

dominant seventh chord – seventh chord built off the 5th scale degree

double flat (♭♭) – a flat lowered an additional half step

double sharp (×) – a sharp raised an additional half step

dynamics – indication of the loudness or softness of a composition; volume at which music is performed

fanfare – instrumental piece or section of music, often ceremonial and played by brass instruments

figured bass – bass line marked to indicate harmonies to be played with each note; commonly associated with Baroque music

folk music – popular music of its day

funeral march – slow march, usually in a minor key

fusion – a.k.a. jazz-rock; music genre combining jazz improvisation and chord progressions with the rhythms of rock

harmonic interval – interval created when two pitches are played/sung at the same time

harmonic minor – natural minor scale with a raised 7th

harmonic texture – method of organizing melody based on interval relationships

Harmonie – "in-house" instrumental group of eight, performing for nobility

interval – distance between two pitches

jazz – form of popular music with a heavy use syncopation and frequent employment of improvisation in performance

jazz-rock – a.k.a. fusion; music genre combining jazz improvisation and chord progressions with the rhythms of rock

jongleur – traveling Medieval performer who entertained with music, dance, juggling, and tricks

Lauds – early morning recitations for church that involve music

libretto – text of an opera

loud ensemble – Medieval instrumental music group predominantly including precursors to modern brass family instruments

madrigal – Renaissance musical form that reflected emotional intimacy with vernacular text

major triad – triad composed of a major third on the bottom and a minor third on the top

Mass – church service in which music is used

melodic interval – interval created when two pitches are played/sung one after the other

melodic minor – minor scale (written both ascending and descending) whose ascending scale is a natural minor scale with a raised 6th and 7th, and whose descending scale is simply a natural minor scale

minor interval – interval created when the second pitch of a major interval is lowered by a half step

minor scale – scale consisting of eight pitches in a pattern of whole and half steps determined by its variety (see harmonic minor, melodic minor, natural minor)

minor triad – triad composed of a minor third on the bottom and a major third on the top

minstrel – traveling Medieval performer who entertained with music, dance, juggling, and tricks

minuet – musical form in $\frac{3}{4}$ to accompany a dance

music program – curriculum of music in a school system

nationalism – movement characterized by greater use of folk music, legendary historical subject matter, dance, and overall native cultural flavor

natural minor – scale using the same pitches of a major scale, but using the 6th scale degree of the major scale as its root

neoclassicism – modern music displaying characteristics of music from the Classical Period

neoromanticism – modern music displaying characteristics of music from the Romantic Period

octave – an interval of an eighth; both pitches in an octave have the same letter name

opera – dramatic musical production combining elaborate sets and costumes

oratorio – form of music drama based on religious subjects

perfect interval – interval between the first scale degree of a major scale and the unison, fourth, fifth, and octave

programme music – music that depicts stories or scenes

recitative – musically reciting the text of an opera drama

relative major – major scale that shares its key signature with a minor scale

relative minor – minor scale that shares its key signature with a major scale

repetition and contrast – important organizational method in composing Renaissance music

rhythm and blues – urban music style of blues that included electric instruments, drums, piano, saxophones, brass, and vocalists

rock – music genre that grew out of the rich tradition of American popular music, especially the blues, and including electric instruments; a freer form of rock and roll that uses more electric amplification and distortion of sound, and offers more room for improvisation

rock and roll – popular music genre of the 20h century, combining rhythm and blues and country music

seventh chord – chord composed of a root, third, fifth, and seventh

soft ensemble – Medieval instrumental music group primarily including flutes, recorders, lutes, and keyboards

solo concerto – Classical musical form that evolved from the Baroque concerto grosso; concerto featuring only one soloist

symphony – popular large-scale instrumental musical form during the Classical and Romantic Periods

synthesizer – musical instrument that can reproduce the human voice and other sounds electronically

triad – three pitches sounding simultaneously in which each pitch is an interval of a third apart, and which is named after its root

unison – the same pitch; two people singing the same pitch are singing in unison

variations (on a theme) – recurring simple melodic themes in different forms

Vespers – evening prayer service for church that involves music

virtuoso – extremely skilled singer or instrumentalist